KU-545-711

the Girl Guide

Annual 1986

edited by
Rosalind
Woodhouse

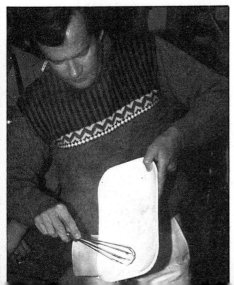

This annual belongs to ...

Jill

COOKING
with Glynn Christian

Two Guides, Clare Smith and Melanie Gwilliams, from the 9th Chelsea (Oratory) Company and I met Glynn Christian at his garden flat near London's Notting Hill Gate. Some of you may have seen Glynn on BBC's *Breakfast Time* television. A couple of times a week, this descendant of Fletcher Christian of the *Bounty* fame, enthusiastically passes on culinary hints and recipes. We were there to learn how to make choux pastry, rough puff pastry and to try something completely new to us, painting on pastry.

Glynn, Clare and Melanie made the choux pastry first. Many people think choux pastry is very difficult, but we were to see that this is not so!

By Debbie Scholes
Photographs by Tony Rose

*Glynn Christian says that with practice you will find that recipes do not have to be followed word for word. Ingredients and conditions can be varied from day to day.

Glynn weighs out the ingredients.

Don't let your butter burn!

Adding the flour and salt to the melted butter.

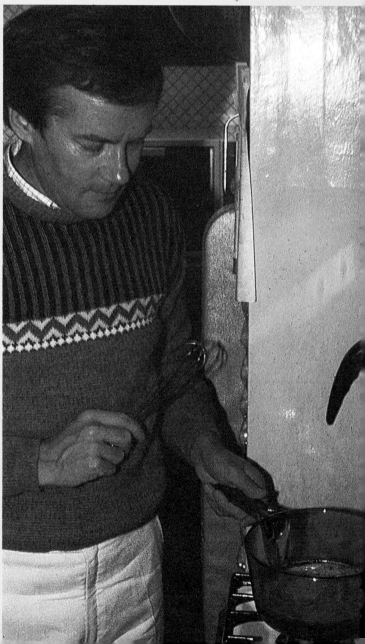

The following ingredients for choux pastry will make about 24 buns.
You will need:
½ pint (300 ml) water
4 oz (100 g) butter
1 oz (25 g) white sugar (if making sweet pastry)
5 oz (150 g) plain strong white flour
a pinch of salt
4 eggs, beaten

The amount of water in this recipe is very important; it should be exactly ½ pint (300 ml).
*Glynn Christian says that if you are very careful you can measure out the water when it is boiling, because if you measure the water first and then boil it, a small amount will evaporate as steam.

The butter was added to the water and left over a low heat until it melted. The water was then boiled, the sugar added and dissolved, and then the sieved flour and salt. Our chefs took the pan from the hob and stirred the mixture until it formed a ball. They returned the pan to the heat and turned the mixture gently for about 30 seconds, then it was left to cool down.
*Glynn Christian says that it helps to have two people for the next part of the method, as beating the eggs is hard work!

Mix to form a ball.

Clare finds that beating in the eggs takes stamina

– and a team effort!

Space the buns well apart, so they don't join up during cooking.

Glynn starts to shape the pastry into a rectangle.

Adding the liquid to the dry ingredients.

Raw pastry tastes *bad*!

Each of them took it in turns to beat in the eggs, one by one. The mixture must be beaten really smooth between each egg. The girls then spooned dollops of the pastry on to a wet baking tray. ***Glynn Christian says, use a wet baking tray as the steam it produces helps the choux pastry to rise.**

To make the choux buns shiny when cooked, Glynn brushed them carefully with a little egg yolk and water mixture.

The buns are baked for 15–25 minutes at gas mark 6/400°F/200°C. When they were crisp and golden they were taken out.

*Glynn Christian says, at this stage make a small hole in each bun and replace them in the oven at the lowest temperature for about ten minutes. This helps to dry out the insides.

When the buns were cooked they were filled with cream. ***Glynn Christian says, to make them a little more homemade-looking, break them open slightly and spoon in the whipped cream, instead of piping it.**

The buns were then piled into a tower on a plate and melted chocolate was poured over them.

*Glynn Christian says, melt chocolate in a heat resistant bowl over hot water.

When we had eaten the choux buns with great relish, it was time to make the rough puff pastry. For this we needed:
8 oz (225 g) strong plain flour
a small pinch of salt
4 oz (100 g) soft margarine or butter
4 oz (100 g) soft lard
½ tablespoon lemon juice made up to ¼ pint (150 ml) with very cold water

Our chefs sieved the flour and salt into a mixing bowl. Then they cut the fat into small pieces and added it to the flour. When this was mixed, a well was made in the centre and the lemon juice and water poured in. This was mixed in with a palette knife, making sure that the flour was well blended.

Glynn and the Guides placed the mixture on to a floured board and moulded it into a brick shape, which was then gently rolled in strokes away from the body, keeping the short end of the brick nearest the body. When the dough measured about 16″ × 5″ (40 cm × 12 cm) it was folded into three. First the third nearest the body was folded over the middle third, then the last third over those two. Glynn tapped the open edges gently to trap the air.
*Glynn Christian says, rough puff pastry won't cook in layers unless the air is trapped.

The dough was turned round one quarter turn and we left it to rest for one minute. We repeated the rolling and folding three times, each time giving the dough a quarter turn, with Melanie and Clare both having a go at rolling it out.
*Glynn Christian says, now chill the pastry in the fridge, before you roll it out to the shape you want.

Rolling out the pastry.

A well-floured work surface prevents the pastry sticking.

Glynn demonstrates how to fold the pastry.

Melanie gently presses the open edges together.

Glynn brushes beaten egg yolk over the pastry to ensure a shiny finish when cooked.

Food dyes can be mixed to give any colour you like.

The impressive end results.

After the pastry had been taken out of the frldge, it was rolled out into a large rectangular shape which was then cut into smaller rectangles.
*Glynn Christian says, being very careful, you should cut the pastry with the sharpest knife possible as with anything else the air is pushed out.

This pastry was going to be painted, so the cooks cut shapes in the tops of the rectangles (but not too deeply). They cut stripes, dlamond shapes, and one piece of pastry they cut into a fish shape. This could then be filled with creamed tuna or salmon when cooked.

The painting was done with lots of different coloured food dyes. The three chefs, who now turned into artists, used blue, green, red, orange and pink. The dyes were painted on very carefully with an ordinary clean paint brush. The brush must be washed very carefully between each colour

and dried well.
*Glynn Christian says, don't use too much dye as, with a fatty pastry such as this, the dye may run.

To make the colours really glossy when dry, they were painted with egg yolk. The finished product can be sliced and filled with anything, from creamed mushrooms to confectioners' custard.

The Light of Liberty

By Simon Shaw
Illustrated by Bob Hersey

She's got a 10.7 m (420 in) waist, and a 1.38 m (4 ½ ft) long nose; one of her fingers alone is 2.4 m (8 ft) long and more than 1 m (3 ft) round, and each of her fingernails is 25 cm (10 in) wide.

In spite of such gigantic measurements, she's the best-loved lady in the whole of America, and she is known the whole world over as the Statue of Liberty.

This famous landmark, which stands in the middle of New York harbour, is 100 years old this year, and there will be celebrations all over America to mark its birthday.

In order to give anyone who has not actually seen this huge statue an idea of its size, more than 40 people can stand together on her hand, and the powerful light from her torch can be seen easily from a distance of 32 km (20 miles).

Many of you will think that this statue was made in America, but it started out in France. It was a special gift from the people of France to the people of America to celebrate the centenary of the Declaration of Independence of 1776. Work began on the statue in 1876 in Paris, and by 1886 the statue had been completed and erected in America.

The man who created the statue was Frederic Auguste Bartholdi, and the figure of a woman holding a light in her hand was to symbolize liberty lighting up the world. It was an expensive undertaking. It cost the French people a quarter of a million dollars to build, and the American public gave an equal sum to build a solid pedestal for it. When ready, it was packed into 214 separate cases and crates and shipped to New York in a French warship.

As it arrived, the American people gave it a tremendous welcome. American warships escorted the French ship into the harbour, which was black with people who wanted to see the statue. Thousands of small boats sailed beside the French warship during the last few miles of its voyage to New York, all sounding their sirens as a rousing welcome to the famous statue.

Bartholdi had already decided where the statue was to stand. He had previously visited New York, and wanted it to be put on Bedloe's Island, a tiny piece of land off the southern tip of the harbour, renamed Liberty Island, so that all ships coming into the harbour and leaving it would see the magnificent statue.

For six months, 75 men worked on the statue, putting it together. They used 300,000 rivets to put the 200 parts of the statue into place, finishing with the huge torch.

To honour the statue, an American poet – Emma Lazarus – wrote a poem to engrave inside the pedestal, and five lines of it have become world-famous:

Give me your tired, your poor,
Your wretched masses yearning to be free,
The wretched refuse of your teeming shore,
Send them, the homeless, tempest tossed to me,
I light the lamp beside the golden door!

These lines of poetry were to welcome the thousands and thousands of people from all over the world who came to America over the years to seek freedom and a better way of life.

When the Statue of Liberty was unveiled to the American people on 28th October 1886, there was no sign of Bartholdi, who should have been in a place of honour with a speech to read. But when the enormous French flag was flown from the head of the statue, he was seen inside the statue pulling the cord which lowered the flag for the crowds to see the face of the Statue of Liberty for the first time.

Today, you can see a smaller version of the Statue of Liberty in Paris standing near one of the bridges over the River Seine.

In 1924, the statue was listed as a national monument by the American government, and visitors are allowed to climb up the iron staircase inside the figure and look out over the harbour from the observation platform. Every year, some two million people go by boat from New York harbour to visit the statue, and they are amazed by its size as well as the fact that the torch uses 2,000 watts of electricity to light up.

In all, over 50 million people have visited the statue since 1886, and the poem inside is probably the most widely-read piece of poetry in the world.

Today, it's impossible to estimate the value of the Statue of Liberty since it is a symbol of freedom and hope for people all over the world, as well as for Americans. Those who have sailed into New York beneath the shadow of the Statue of Liberty have seen in it a promise of personal freedom and a better future for everyone the whole world over.

make your own

By Jil Shipley

Jewellery doesn't have to be expensive! You can make lots of unusual necklaces, brooches and earrings using everyday objects and leather thonging or coloured cord. You can buy brooch pins and earring clips from Art and Craft shops and there are lots of good strong glues around —— we used UHU

Art and Craft shops sell a modelling material which you harden in the oven (FIMO). It comes in brilliant, mixable colours and is very easy to use. Make delightfully uneven beads in slightly different shades, or funny brooches (glued onto brooch clips with UHU), or delicate earring - just pierce a hole to hang it from before hardening.

A rectangle of shiny, stiff coloured paper (from art shops or good stationers) can be folded, concertina-fashion, and stitched into a fan-shape. Stick one onto a brooch pin, or hang two or three from an earring clip. You could stick some coloured beads over the stitching.

Pasta 'wheels' can be threaded like this

onto thin satin ribbon or cord.

Paint pasta 'bows' with bright coloured enamel (Humbrol do lots of colours, in tiny pots, from model shops) and tie them onto a leather thong or piece of bright cord, or hang one from an earring clip.

Jewellery

Toy shops yield great finds! Tiny plastic or wooden animals can be tied with coloured cord and hung from earring clips or worn on thonging as necklaces.

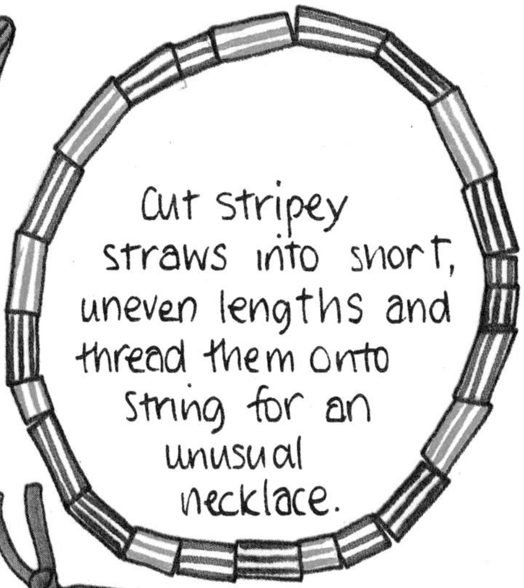

Cut stripey straws into short, uneven lengths and thread them onto string for an unusual necklace.

Toy shops also sell huge wooden beads — thread them onto thonging with a knot between each bead.

Feathers — from woods or parks or Mums feather duster — look great tied onto a length of coloured cord, threaded with a few beads and fastened onto a pony-tail band,

or tie a little satin ribbon in a bow around the ball of the pony-tail band. Thread coloured beads onto the ends.

Macaroni can be painted and threaded onto string or elastic.

Thin brass rings, threaded onto a length of canvas or leather make an interesting belt.

Thread them on like this ⟶

JIL SHIPLEY

By Doris Bellringer
Illustrated by Peter Cornwell

"Come on, Sue," called Elaine, "we'd better have an early night."

"Good idea," agreed their mother.

Tomorrow was the day of the 4th Heasehill Guides' pantomine. Elaine, P.L. of the Robins, was playing Widow Twankey and her younger sister Sue, the back legs of the cow.

"You're hoping Peter Banks will notice you, aren't you?" whispered Sue as they reached the bedroom.

"What if I am," snapped Elaine.

"I was only saying," muttered Sue, but she knew better than to pursue the subject.

At first Elaine had been disappointed when she had been cast for Widow Twankey and her best friend Helen had been selected to play Aladdin, but as she worked at the part she began to realise its possibilities.

When even the Guides laughed at her performance she felt she was really achieving success.

She and Helen were both keen on drama and secretly wanted to make the stage a career. Secretly, because neither was given any encouragement from teachers or parents.

"Only a few get to the top" and "very precarious profession" seemed to be the opinions of most adults, so both girls kept quiet about their real ambitions. When they discovered that the uncle of one of the Guides was director of the local Little Theatre and had promised his niece he would come to see *Aladdin* you can imagine their excitement.

Helen, who had a lovely singing voice, had played Dorothy in the school production of *The Wizard of Oz*, while Elaine had been a great success as St Joan in their recent production of Shaw's play. Her performance had even been compared favourably with Frances de la Tour's portrayal in the West End and the cutting from the local paper was one of her most treasured possessions.

She was thinking, as she prepared for bed, that tomorrow might prove to be her lucky day. Perhaps she would be noticed by Peter Banks and accepted as a junior member of the newly formed Little Theatre Dramatic Society.

"Goodnight, Sue," she yawned, and settled down to dream of success.

She had not been asleep for long when she was awakened by groans coming from Sue's bed.

"What's up?" she called, but instead of answering, Sue rushed from the room.

The bathroom door crashed open and Elaine could hear her being violently sick. After some time she returned, shivering, and tottered back to bed.

Elaine got up, filled two hot water bottles, put one at Sue's feet and gave her the other to cuddle.

"Thanks," murmured Sue, "I feel awful," then she curled up and fell asleep almost immediately.

Elaine wasn't so fortunate. She lay awake listening. Someone else was in and out of the bathroom. It sounded as thought both her parents were feeling ill. Elaine knew she should be feeling sorry for them but was much more concerned with herself. She prayed and prayed that she would be good enough for Peter Banks to offer her a place but knew that now she's be tired and probably give a dull performance.

She tossed and turned for what seemed like hours then fell into a troubled sleep until late morning. Even then she was the only one moving, the only one in the family who had escaped the tummy upsets of the night. No one wanted any food but Elaine prepared a snack for herself and left, very late, to help with the final preparations at the hall.

The sky was heavy with snow and the wind was biting as she fought her way to the meeting place. The hall door was caught by the wind and slammed shut, drowning her voice as she called, "Where's Bee?"

She stamped her feet and shook the snow from her hat and coat. Bee, the Guider, emerged from the kitchen with a plate of cakes. "You're late, but thank goodness you've come, Elaine. Where's Sue?"

"Sorry, Bee, Sue can't come, she's still in bed. The whole family have tummy upsets – all except me. Don't know whether it's a virus or something they've eaten but no one had much sleep last night."

"That's three Guides away, and no one to do the makeup. You'll have to start on the Brownies. Most of them are here and they're a *wee bit* excited, if you know what I mean."

"Right," answered Elaine, and for the next hour-and-a-half she was busy slapping rouge, lipstick and eye shadow on courtiers, pages and ladies-in-waiting. She repaired the wings of a fairy and the tail of a rabbit, borrowed cocoa from the kitchen and browned the hands of two trees who were to wear masks but didn't want to be left out of the makeup excitement. She made silver foil claws for the witch and put a plaster on the finger of a squirrel who insisted she'd been caught in a snare.

Helen, looking smart as usual in spite of the weather, was helping in the kitchen. She had found time to change into her costume, do her own makeup and was already greeting the VIPs as they came in for the performance

Elaine hastily finished her own makeup and peeped through the curtain. Helen was being especially charming to Peter Banks. Elaine felt a sudden panic. Her legs went weak, she felt ill, rushed to the loo and was sick. As she recovered she took deep breaths and knew, just knew, she'd forget her words. This was the chance of a lifetime, her opportunity to be considered for a place with a real drama group and she'd missed it. She dragged herself to the dressing room and was more depressed than ever when she looked

in the mirror. She knew she'd give a dreadful performance and couldn't imagine how she had ever thought she could be funny.

"Elaine, Elaine!" Bee was calling. "Where are you? Come on, the curtain's going up."

Elaine produced a very wintry smile and staggered on stage. She acted in a kind of daze but at least she didn't dry up, and even managed to get a laugh or two, until at last it was over. The cast took their curtain calls and Elaine breathed a sigh of relief. At least she'd not been sick on stage. Her inside was churning and her one desire now was to get home and go to bed.

As she was leaving the hall, who should she bump into but Peter Banks! She tried to slip past him but he took her hands.

"Helen tells me you're anxious to work in the theatre. I won't pretend your performance tonight was marvellous, but the way you've helped backstage and carried on with your part in spite of feeling so unwell, now that's the sort of person we want in the theatre, and I'd be delighted to give you a place in our new company if that's what you'd like."

Elaine felt herself getting red in the face and blushing right down her neck. "Are you giving a place to Helen as well?" she asked.

"Not at the moment. Helen has a sweet voice. I think she'll do well, but it needs a lot of training. You don't have to decide now, but if you'd care to come along next Thursday evening we'll all be pleased to see you."

"I'll come, of course I'll come, I don't need to think about it. Thank you, oh thank you!" But Peter Banks had disappeared into the crowd.

PUZZLES

By Ann Hillyer

WHO DOES WHAT?

Four members of the Swallow Patrol – Deborah, Suzy, Juliet and Helen – attend various activities on Saturday mornings. Their Captain kindly gives them a lift into town.

Each girl's class is held at a different place, and all start at intervals of 15 minutes, the first at 10 am. From the information given, can you find out which Guide attends which activity, where and when?

– The Roller Disco starts half an hour after First Aid; neither takes place at the Sports Centre.
– Deborah is dropped off first at the Chapel Hall.
– Traffic is heavy – Juliet worries she will not reach the Youth Club in time.
– Helen's trampolining starts at 10.45 am.
– The Badminton class starts at 10.15 am.
– Suzy does not go to the class in the School Hall.

BIRD, BEAST OR FISH?

In each sentence there is hidden the name of a bird, animal or fish. See if you can find them all. One sentence contains TWO hidden names!
1. They both rushed into the meadow.
2. You should see our new house, Alice!
3. Is there a bench or seat to sit on?
4. We can't take her on holiday with us this time.
5. Jill's tennis is good, but she lobs terribly.
6. Sew on this badge really firmly.
7. The River Dee runs through Cheshire.
8. Amy was the star linguist on the trip to France.
9. Write a letter to a dear friend.
10. Poor Mary lost her ring at the swimming pool.

ROUND IN CIRCLES

By taking alternative letters, find the names of two popular sports or pastimes in each of the five different-coloured circles. The tricky part is finding which letter to start with!

Answers on page 63.

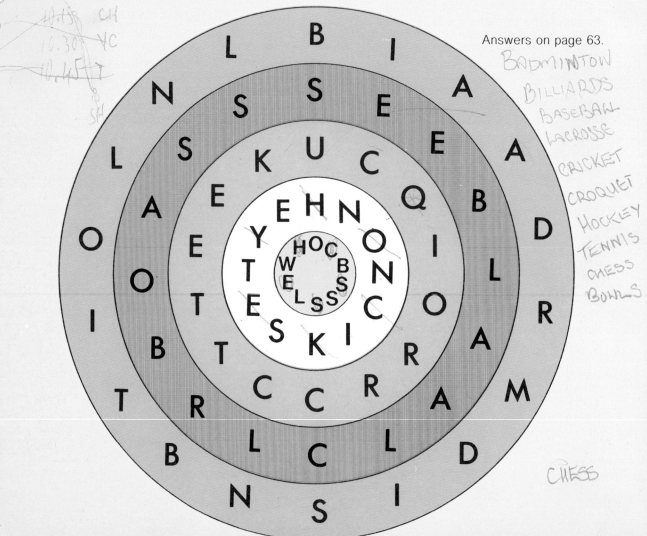

14

Kingfishers for Company

Written and photographed
by Michael Edwards

We often compare British birds unfairly with their colourful tropical counterparts, but our kingfisher comes second to none in the beauty stakes.

I remember as a child of nine seeing my first kingfisher while picnicking by a local river. A streak of electric blue was the only glimpse I had of the fisherman as he sped by. Since that day I have always wanted to meet the bird on its home ground at close quarters. Last summer, I realised my ambition by studying a pair of these gorgeous birds – my ultimate aim being to photograph the elusive fisherman in his trout stream home.

The birds were eventually located along the river's willow-lined banks. My search proper began in February. During the winter, male and female lived separate lives along different parts of the river, but as spring approached they came together to establish a breeding territory.

Kingfishers, basically, are rather silent birds in that they have no song as such, but in March as the barometer rose, they would utter a range of whistles and trillings to warn all other kingfishers that this stretch of the river was occupied.

Having found a suitable sandy bank, both birds began to throw themselves at it quite vigorously, displacing the sand until a ledge had been formed on which they could stand and bore deep into the bank.

The completed nest tunnel, which sloped gently upwards to a round chamber, was almost 1m (3ft) long. Excavations had taken just over one week and a few days later the female had laid the first of her eight round, white eggs. Both sexes took turns to incubate and the first chick, naked and blind, hatched out about 20 days later.

Before I could disturb the breeding kingfishers, I was sent a licence by the Nature Conservancy Council which gave me permission to photograph the birds, which are specially protected under the First Schedule of rarer British birds. To disturb them near the nest is against the law, unless permission is granted.

I visited the river with a friend where a camouflaged observation and photographic hide had been erected some days before and moved closer to the study area each day so as not to alarm our subjects.

We noticed that three overhanging branches were rather worn in places due, we hoped, to the kingfishers' gripping feet.

A hide on the bank would have been useless; the birds would be too small in the picture – if they decided to use the perch with a camera looking on. So the final position of the hide was actually in the river margin. Had we had a wet summer, photography from such a position would have been impossible.

The colour of a kingfisher's wings varies according to how the light strikes them and also on the strength of the light. On cloudy, bright days they often show emerald green, but with the full sun on them the familiar steel blue comes into view.

This calm, tree-lined pool was a favourite haunt of my kingfisher pair.

The camouflaged canvas hide was erected in the river margin. At one stage, a kingfisher actually perched on the guy line nearest the camera.

A kingfisher triumphantly holds aloft its catch – a minnow. Large fish are beaten on the perch to subdue them, or to flatten the spines in the case of a stickleback. Some young kingfishers choke through lack of the latter knowledge.

This tree-root protruding from the river bank was a favourite perch from which the kingfishers studied the water for food. "I could almost see the concentration on his colourful face."

There is a very noticeable pale blue streak extending from the nape to the stubby tail. On the throat and sides of the neck is a patch of white. In flight, the warm chestnut underparts are hidden.

Although they prefer the moving waters of streams and rivers, they will also visit large ponds, canals and flooded gravel pits. A few years ago a pair of these birds bred on the edge of a large housing estate by a water-filled ditch.

We found the lack of water on our river to our advantage and so did the kingfishers. It meant that the minnows and stone loaches on which they were chiefly feeding became easier to catch as the water-level dropped.

Being a trout stream, we were concerned over disturbance to the birds from anglers, but we need not have been. The low water kept most fishermen away – except, we hoped, the ones we wanted to see.

It was 5 am on a still summer morning when we reached the river laden with photographic equipment. The sun shone but did not penetrate the river's tree-lined banks. As we walked along the stream edge a kingfisher shot downstream, uttering its familiar call.

My camera, fitted with a telephoto lens to enable me to take close-up photographs from a distance, was fixed to a tripod, then positioned inside the hide, its legs firmly embedded in the river mud for extra stability. Behind that, a stool for yours truly, who must have been the only person wearing wellingtons when the temperature later reached the 80s. My friend walked away from the hide after I had entered. This would make the kingfishers think that there was no one around, as most birds cannot count.

An hour passed without so much as a glimpse of my subject, as did a further 75 minutes without a sighting. But the time spent waiting was never boring. At that time in the morning many other birds, having taken part in the dawn chorus, were down at the water's edge quenching their thirsts and tidying their plumage.

A moorhen, which had just hatched her eggs in a nest amongst the trailing willow branches, dropped an eggshell over the side. It floated a little way downstream before becoming filled with water and sinking.

A dipper flew upstream in a hurry, calling all the time, ignoring a large mossy stone which is its favourite resting place. Perhaps he had just become a parent and couldn't wait to see his new family.

A family party of blue tits pecked about the muddy margin, while a pair of carrion crows croaked in the canopy above

It is only when you see him perched that the rich chestnut underparts are seen. Male and female kingfishers are almost identical.

The stream was an exclusive trout water – unfortunately, kingfishers can't read.

before descending to drink. A mallard duck, uneasy with the crows so close, escorted her brown and yellow baby corks downstream out of harm's way.

Damselflies, those red and blue flying needles, were everywhere looking for mates, and below the surface while the kingfishers were away, minnows played hide-and-seek amongst the stones and weed.

It was 7.45. Suddenly, there was a *chee, chee* and the male kingfisher was back on his favourite perch. The living jewel was just 3 m (10 ft) before me, his head cocked to one side as though listening for something. He took no notice of the camera at all. There was a brief excited posture in which he opened and closed his beak while quivering his wings.

His mate had just flashed past.

But he was hungry. His attention was drawn to the clear, unpolluted shallows below. One could almost see the concentration on his colourful face. Then he was gone – returning in the blink of an eye with a caddis larva in his beak. This was juggled about before being dropped. The next dive brought up a minnow. He manipulated the fish, I released the camera's shutter, and he swallowed his catch headfirst.

He then sped off upstream. On his return ten minutes later his mate was waiting. That could only mean one thing – the nestlings were ready for feeding. She rejoined her family deep in the river-bank, taking a tiny minnow with her, leaving her husband to fish.

He sped off downstream but was gone only for a short time. I heard him call, but I could not see him anywhere. He would frequently perch on large boulders on the other side of the stream before flying on to his favourite perch to fish, but he was nowhere to be seen. Then, peering though the canvas weave of my hide, I 'froze' – I dared not breathe, for the kingfisher in all his finery was perched 35 cm (14 in) from my nose, his brilliant red feet clutching one of the hide's guy lines!

After what seemed like ages, but was probably only about ten seconds, he flew to a more convenient perch and caught two minnows in six dives. The first fish he swallowed, craftily looking back to see if his wife wasn't watching, the second was taken to feed his family.

But I had taken a number of pictures . . . and the memory of the day when I was nose to beak with our most colourful bird is an experience I shall never forget.

By Jill Weekes   Illustrated by Shelagh McGee

Whether you struggle with the simplest sewing stitches, or turn out exquisite embroidery, you would get nowhere without your needle, that vital strip of metal with which you guide the thread.

Needles have been around since man first invented tools. The very first needles, which had no eyes, were pieces of thorn, flint or bone. By the early Stone Age, however, splinters of bone were used, with eyes to hold the thread. By 100 B C, iron needles had appeared. Interestingly, although some bone needles can be seen in museums today, very few iron needles survived, as they just rusted away!

As the centuries passed, needle making was carried on mainly in the monasteries. By the time the monasteries had been disbanded by King Henry VIII, the trade had spread to London. Needlers Lane and Threadneedle Street were named after the craftsmen who worked there. Needle making workshops also stood on the old London Bridge.

After the Great Fire of London in 1666, many needlemakers left the city and settled in the Buckinghamshire countryside. Gradually, they moved to Warwickshire, which has been an important centre for needle making ever since.

How Needles are Made

They start life in pairs, rather like Siamese twins! A soft piece of steel wire is straightened from a coil, and cut to the length of two needles. Both ends are pointed, and two eye impressions are stamped in the centre of the wire. A hole is then punched through each central eye, and the wire is broken into two separate needles. When the waste metal round the eye has been ground off, the wire is hardened, and adjusted to make sure each needle is flexible enough. After the needles have been cleaned, smoothed, highly polished and plated with nickel, each one is individually inspected before being packed.

Types of Needles

Needles come in so many lengths, widths and eye-sizes,

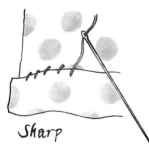

Sharp

Crewel needle

Darner

Bodkin

you may well feel you are searching for a needle in a haystack, unless you know what to look for!

The *sharps* are the ordinary household needles, used for all kinds of general sewing. They have short, round eyes to give them extra strength: the thickest is a size 1 and the thinnest, size 12.

Embroidery or crewel needles are the same as sharps, but have longer eyes to take several strands of embroidery silk. Size 1 is the thickest, size 10 the thinnest.

You almost certainly know the *darners*, long, thick needles, with long eyes to take woollen darning thread. This time, the thickest is size 14 and the thinnest, size 9. Among their cousins, *long darners*, the thickest is size 15, the thinnest size 9.

You may have used *bodkins*, which are flat or round needles, with blunt ends and extra large eyes, for threading cord, tape and elastic. Bodkins come in size 17 only.

Tapestry and *chenille* needles are used with wool or embroidery cotton on canvas or tapestry fabric. Both have extra large eyes to take thick wool and silks. Tapestry needles are blunt, while chenille needles have sharp points. Tapestry needles range from size 13 (the thickest) to size 26; chenille needles from size 13, to the thinnest, size 24.

You are perhaps less likely to use *betweens* or *quilting* needles. They have small eyes like sharps, but are shorter, for quick, even stitching. Tailors and professional sewers use them. They range from size 1, the thickest, to size 10.

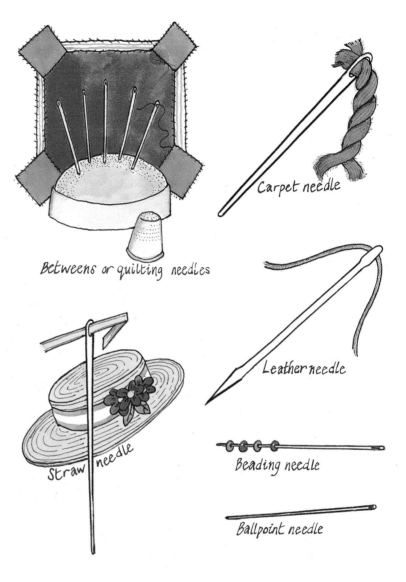

Carpet needle

Betweens or quilting needles

Leather needle

Straw needle

Beading needle

Ballpoint needle

Milliners' or *straw* needles are long, with round eyes, and are used for work on hats and bonnets. They can also be used for pleating and decoration on dresses. Size 15 is the thickest, size 10 the thinnest.

Carpet needles, like heavy sharps, are used to sew rugs and carpets. They come in just three sizes: 16 (the thickest), 17 and 18.

Leather needles sew gloves, belts, leather, vinyl and plastic garments. They have triangular points, which pierce the fabric without tearing it. Size 1 is thickest, size 8 thinnest.

You may not have seen *beading* and *ball point sewing* needles. Beading needles are very fine and straight with long eyes, and are

specially made to thread beads and pearls. Ball point sewing needles have rounded points, for use on jersey and synthetic materials. The thickest beading needle is size 10 and the thinnest size 15; the thickest ball point sewing needle is size 5 and the thinnest size 10.

But if you spend more time losing your thread than pushing it through the material, you will be glad to hear there is an *easy-threading* needle! Instead of struggling to poke the thread through that tiny hole, you simply slot it through a small gap at the base of the eye. You can choose from sizes 4 (the thickest), 6 or 8 — so really, there is no need for sewing to needle you!

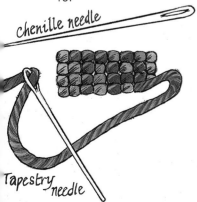

chenille needle

Tapestry needle

A Walk on the Roof

At Pokhara, on the edge of a large dusty field where schoolchildren joined in an enormous game of football, we ate our packed lunch — the last link with the city — while porters walked out from the town to be employed by our Sirdar, the chief Sherpa, to carry our stores and baggage. Sacred cows really do wander wherever they wish, and one came to see what we had left; she was quite happy with cardboard boxes!

After a day and a half of sightseeing in the brilliant March sunshine of Kathmandu, we were riding with six Sherpas in an expedition truck on the drive to Pokhara where the trek would begin. The six-hour drive seemed much shorter, as we saw something interesting every mile of the way and listened to the songs of the Sherpas. The climb out of the Kathmandu valley and down the spectacular hairpin bends was exciting enough even without imagining what it must be like to ride on the roof of the public bus.

Whenever the truck slowed down, people came out with trays of oranges to sell and once when we stopped in a village street, a beggar sang and played. His violin seemed clumsy, carved from a solid piece of wood, but he made sprightly music that sounded a little like a Scottish jig.

The Sherpas said that we would reach our first camping place in two hours. We strode along a dusty, stony track beside a river where a big dam was being built and felt quite proud when we arrived in 1½ hours.

The Sherpas smiled gently. "You're going too fast," they said quietly.

In a few days, they, the sun and the steep path taught us the best pace to use.

Written and photographed by Nannette Simmons

At first we walked westward towards Kali Gandaki – the Black River – where we would turn north to walk for five days through a deep gorge between two great mountains, Annapurna and Dhaulagiri, nearly as high as Everest. This is part of an ancient trade route to Tibet and it is still in use, so the path is very well made and maintained. When rivers have to be crossed there are bridges made of strong steel cables slung across the gorge carrying metal loops which support planks of wood. They had all been rebuilt the year before, but they still swung in a most exciting way when we crossed.

The mountains were astonishing; the lower slopes rose in thousands of green terraces where the people grew crops. In other places there were forests of rhododendron trees where it was warm, and pines in colder, higher places. Above these, glistening in the sun like white silk, were all the peaks of Annapurna and Dhaulagiri, crowned with a white veil of snow blown by the wind. We could *feel* how high they were when we had to bend our heads back so far to see them. Sometimes we thought they were lost in the mist, until we realised that the white peaks were shining above the clouds much higher than we had been looking.

everywhere, called by their mother hens who scratched up the dust for them, while the brilliant cocks perched on the walls and crowed.

A village was always a welcome sight because it meant there would be a tea house where we could sit for a while and have a drink. Tea is made on a little fire on the floor. At some houses there are many choices, milk tea in which the tea-leaves, milk, water and sugar are all boiled together; plain black tea, or lemon tea, which was my favourite.

Some of the houses had a Cola sign nailed to the doorway and we could indeed buy bottles of Coke or lemon kept cool in a bucket of water. The bottles got more and more expensive the further we were up the valley, because of course someone had to carry every bottle there. We saw a man at the beginning of the track carrying a load of six trays of Coke, and there are twenty-four bottles in each tray!

Whenever the Nepalese people meet friends or strangers they lift their hands, palms together, and say "Namaste" which is a way of saying "Greetings", "Welcome" or "Hello". The answer is to do the same.

We were thrilled to be included in

this welcome by children going to school, men driving the mule trains and women spinning on their verandahs or washing dishes or their babies at the village water spout . . .

We had to look where we put our feet because tiny chicks ran

There were not many dogs and cats, but those we met never flinched away as some do in other countries; they seemed happy to see us, and when we sat down in their house they often jumped up beside us and enjoyed being stroked. All the animals were treated well. Small children were often out in charge of the family buffalo, taking it to the waterhole for a wallow. A team of mules, donkeys or yaks is a trader's pride and joy. Many of them are dressed with coloured plumes and decorated blankets, and all wear bells so that the moving teams became chiming orchestras that we never tired of hearing.

Our day began at sunrise, about six o'clock, when the cook brought a cup of tea to our tents. We drank it while we gazed out at the mountains. Then we dressed and packed, camera and water bottle in our day pack, sleeping bag and the rest in our kit bag. While we had a quick breakfast of porridge and bread and jam the Sherpas took down the tents and the porters put their loads together. Some men took three of our kit bags plus a tent, and still had energy to sing as they walked, or to show us a monkey in the trees.

We started walking at seven to have a few hours before the sun got hot. Three hours later, when a Sherpa called us, we climbed over a wall into a field where we saw our 'magic carpet', a blue groundsheet spread for us to sit on during lunch: omelettes, curried dumplings and potato cakes with hot lemonade and a piece of cake. This is the time when the Sherpas and porters ate their real breakfast. We had a lazy time basking in the sun until twelve o'clock when we set off again.

On two afternoons the sun disappeared in cloud, thunder boomed among the mountains and big warm drops of rain fell.

The Sherpa girl walking with us was usually very quiet and shy, but when the rain began she started to sing. People in the villages ran up to their terraces to hoe the weeds, and there was a very happy feeling everywhere. Smiling faces looked out, calling us in to shelter when the rain got really heavy. It didn't last long, then the leaves looked glossier and more flowers came out, and we could see a dusting of new snow on the higher slopes.

By four o'clock we began to wonder what our next camping place would be like. We entered one town where the men were holding an archery match in the main street. We usually found one of the porters standing at the door saying, "Here we are. This way," and showing us through to the garden where our tents were pitched and cooking fires lit. While supper cooked, we had time to look around the village and talk to people, until it was dark, at about six o'clock.

After five days in the valley we had come through to the other side of the Himalayas. The landscape is very like Tibet, we were told.

We sat at the edge of the village, gazing north to where Tibet lay, another five days' walk away. Here we were to turn eastward and walk to Muktinath, which is a great pilgrimage place for both Hindus and Buddhists. Springs of holy water run out of 108 spouts shaped like cows' heads and, most mysterious of all, a jet of natural gas burns with a small blue flame in the rock in the peaceful gloom of a small Buddhist temple guarded by a happy Tibetan lady.

We were now 12,000 feet up and very breathless in the thin air, but the sparkling day with snow peaks all around, eagles flying overhead and the joyful atmosphere of the place made up for that. We didn't want to leave. The only consolation was that we had another eight days in the valley.

On the way back we took a different route through fairytale forests of flowering rhododendrons, and magnolias filled with birdsong. We all felt reluctant to return to the city, but since the city was Kathmandu and we had a few more hours there we were soon enjoying its magic again, where even ordinary houses are carved like palaces and flute sellers make music in the streets.

Make a Collage Card

By Barbara Blease

Collect together:
1 piece of paper 30 cm × 21 cm;
1 piece of card 30 cm × 21 cm;
paints: poster or watercolours;
paint brush; pencil; scissors;
glue: Copydex, PVA medium or
one of the white, clear drying
wood glues; felt pens.

The fist step is to produce a
multi-coloured paper from which
you can cut flower petal shapes.
To do this, wet the piece of paper
thoroughly, either by holding it
under a running tap or by wiping
it with a well-soaked cloth. Then
with your wet paper on a flat
surface, drop blobs of different
coloured paint onto the wet
surface. The paints will spread
outwards and merge with each
other in fascinating random
patterns. Allow the paper to dry
before you draw ten pansy petal
shapes on the coloured sheet.
Draw them in areas where you
find the most attractive colour
combinations, then cut them out
carefully.
Fold the piece of card in half.
Assemble five petal shapes to
form a complete flower. Try
different coloured petals until you
have the most attractive
combination. Now you are ready
to stick them to the card. The
important thing to remember is
not to glue down the edges of the
petals, but to allow them to turn
up. This will give the flowers a
realistic appearance.

You will see from the picture and
your own observations that the
petals overlap and lie over one
another; glue yours down in a
similar manner. When the glue is
dry, carefully paint in the stalks
and leaves to join up with the
flowers. Perhaps some of the
flowers will need an extra touch
of paint to complete the
arrangement. Leave the card
until the paint is absolutely dry.

Now is the time to add the
caption 'Happy Birthday' or
'Congratulations' to the front of
the card. A felt pen is probably
best for this.

24

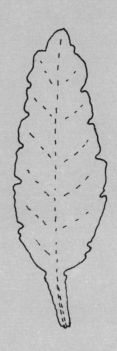

Finally paint the pansy carefully
with a thin coat of glue. When the
glue dries it will leave a clear
transparent film over the flower,
and give an added lustre to the
colours you have used.

Observe a pansy. Notice the
shape of the leaves. Look at the
petals and leaves and examine
how they are joined to the stalk.

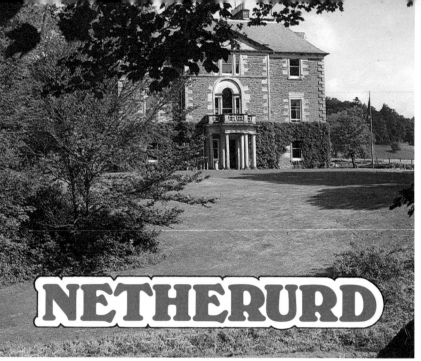

NETHERURD

By Joan Randall

Photographs by Frank and Joan Randall

Let me take you to the Guide House where Guiders, Guides and Brownies from Scotland, and elsewhere, can have fun and trainings.

Major E. G. Thomson MC generously gave Netherurd to The Girl Guides Association in 1952, though it had been used as a training centre since 1945. It is an 18th century mansion, and stands among the gentle hills of the Border Country, eleven miles from Peebles.

You have probably already seen a picture of its unusual gateway, the jaw-bone, or rib, of a whale. *Netherurd* is derived from the Gaelic word 'urd', for 'hill' and 'nether', which means 'the lower part', so the House, situated beneath Shaw Hill, is well named.

All around the area are ancient hill-forts and camps. There was some excitement in 1806 when a herd-boy found a collection of gold ornaments on Shaw Hill, part of Netherurd's land. The then owner, Mr John Lawson, took them to show to his friend Sir Walter Scott, the famous author, whose home, Abbotsford, is nearby.

There are three sites for Patrol camps and three for up to thirty campers.

Elm, beech and sycamore trees grow on the Marquee site. It is divided by a brook, called the Back burn. Endless possibilities for enjoyment here!

The large hut bought in 1953 with a grant from the Baden-Powell Memorial Fund, has given its name to the Hut site, while the Triangle surely needs no explanation!

In the summer, Netherurd's woodlands are bright with rhododendrons. Wild raspberries are there for the gathering. Rosebay Willowherb and other wild flowers are used to make the tall and delightful arrangement in the house. Here in the outdoor oven — an oil drum built into the hillside — Guides can cook sponge puddings and pizzas, with varying results. (The best are covered with tinfoil before baking.)

A Haymaker's Bridge can help you over the burn, but go prepared to get your feet wet.

Geese, ducks, and chickens roam around the grounds and mention must be made of Patchy, the cat that grew up with a corgi and can sit up and beg!

Should you want a public telephone, there it is — in the old deckhouse of a fishing boat.

In the shop, you can buy souvenirs, sweets and ice-creams . . . and the toothpaste you forgot to pack.

Let's go on a tour of the house. On the ground floor are offices, a reception room and a smart new dining room. Two lovely drawing rooms, where conferences and Trainings take place, are found on the first floor.

Some of the bedrooms are here too. Netherurd can sleep forty.

In the room with six beds, a lift has been installed to help the disabled, and the bathroom fittings have been adjusted for their use.

A tiny room at the top of the house is called 'The Porthole' on account of its round window. This is where anyone can go to be quiet, to read, to think . . .

Gifts from home and abroad are kept safely in a glass-fronted cabinet on the landing. Look to your right now. That is a water colour of a Norwegian scene, painted by the Founder, Lord Baden-Powell. It is one of the many treasures. About turn! That wooden bowl and lid, 45cm high, 45cm wide, decorated with carved lizards, monkeys and helmeted warriors, is a West African corn bin.

The Brownie Pack Holiday House is a memorial to Major Thomson's sister-in-law, who was at one time County Commissioner for Peebleshire. The eighteen Brownies who can stay in it have a lawn the size of a hockey pitch to play on. To the side of this is a sundial, but the tiniest can only see what time it is with a little help from her friends!

Rangers, Guiders and their friends can stay in the 'Bothy'. Once a potting-shed, it was transformed, in 1981, into self-contained accommodation for ten, thanks to a legacy from Mrs J. R. C. Greenlees, first President of the Council of Scotland.

Guiders and Guides from all over the world call in on Netherurd and some join the staff for a while.

Within easy reach of Netherurd are many places of interest – Edinburgh, the Border abbeys and castles, the John Buchan Museum, Abbotsford and, of course, Biggar, with the museum where you can touch everything!

So, if you have the opportunity, make tracks for Netherurd. You can be sure of a warm welcome.

A Surprise from Sarah

By Ann Hillyer
Illustrated by Anna Dzierkek

"So don't forget, girls – ten o'clock on Saturday, with brushes and brooms at the ready!"

Captain's voice was merry, but there was a certain firmness in her tone as she added, "Remember, if everyone turns up, we should be finished by midday. If not, it will take much longer."

"I know what Captain means by that," whispered Jenny Wilkins to her friend, Laura Pryde, as they made their way home from the Guide Hall. "She was saying it for the benefit of Stuck-Up Sarah, who never gets her hands dirty if she can help it!"

Laura glanced round quickly, not wanting Sarah to overhear Jenny's pointed remarks, even though she herself agreed with them.

Sarah Moore was the newest addition to the Company. Many of the girls wondered why she had ever become a Guide in the first place. She looked far older than her thirteen years, and was always immaculately dressed, which was a source of amusement to the boisterous Jenny.

"It's all right," chuckled Jenny. "Miss World's still in the cloakroom, making sure she hasn't laddered her precious tights, I expect."

At this, Laura joined in her friend's laughter. The tights Sarah wore had become something of a joke. The younger Guides wore long white socks with their uniform, and the older ones wore the same navy blue tights which they had for school. But Sarah always wore thick cotton tights of a peculiar off-white colour. If ever there was a lively game, or any activity which

involved rushing about, Sarah would keep well back.

"Mind my legs!" mimicked Jenny wickedly, in Sarah's rather nervous, high voice. "Don't ladder my tights, please! They're very difficult to get."

"Flown in specially from Paris, I expect," giggled Laura.

"I can't think why she's so fussy about them," went on Jenny, as they crossed the lane. "They don't look nearly as smart as our navy ones, and she can never join in anything all dressed up like that."

"She doesn't join in much, anyway. Remember how she said she didn't want to come to Camp? Everyone else is coming, even the little Baxter twins."

"Yes, and she didn't come on that trip to the sea at half-term. She missed that beautiful walk along the cliffs, and that delicious swim after!"

"And what about the barbecue that Captain arranged the very first week Sarah came?" added Laura. "She refused point-blank to come to that. It's time you had a word with her, Jenny – she keeps on letting our Patrol down."

"Well, she's not going to wriggle out of Saturday's work party if I can help it," stated Jenny firmly, opening her front gate. "I'll call for you at a quarter to ten, Laura – and don't forget, old clothes!"

"Not cream cotton tights!" replied her friend, laughing.

* * *

"It looks as though Stuck-Up Sarah's let us down again," murmured Laura as she glanced round the hall where the rest of the Guides were hard at work. The White Heathers had taken down the long green curtains and gone to the launderette with them, the Bluebells were stacking chairs, and Jenny's Patrol, the Daffodils, were energetically sweeping the dusty floor before commencing the marathon task of scubbing it.

"Don't tell me!" Jenny's face was stormy. "I reminded her on Thursday at school. I'm going to have a word with Captain and see if Sarah can be moved into another Patrol. It's not fair on us, always being one under strength."

* * *

"Captain," began Jenny, "can't we do something about Sarah? Melissa says she's just seen her going off on the bus –"

"Oh, yes – I had a phone call from Mrs Moore," said Captain thoughtfully. Then she changed the subject. "If you tackle that end of the hall first, Jenny, Melissa and I will try and get the curtains pressed and hung up. Now, where did I put that iron?"

"That's odd," mused Jenny as she and Laura set to work with mops and buckets. "Captain's usually pretty strict with anyone who dodges chores. But she lets Sarah get away with it every time!"

* * *

"I've got a surprise for you, girls," announced Captain at the next Guide meeting. She held up a letter written on thick paper with a crest at the top.

"This is from Lady Cavershaw, whose family gave the money to build this hall. She and her husband came to inspect the hall at the weekend, and were very impressed at the way you gave up your free time to springclean the place. She is a member of the Trefoil Guild, and has always been very interested in Guiding. So next Saturday afternoon she has invited us all to her lovely home, Cavershaw Towers, for swimming and a picnic tea."

Jenny nudged Laura excitedly. Then whe caught sight of Sarah just behind them.

"Captain," asked Jenny, "when you say we're *all* invited, does that mean all of us, or only the ones who helped do the cleaning?"

"All of you. The whole Company is invited."

"Then that's not fair –" burst out Jenny.

"That's enough, Jenny. Come and discuss it with me afterwards. Now then, girls, let's get started on our Trefoil work."

At the end of the meeting, Captain took the irate Jenny on one side.

"It wasn't very kind of you to make a remark like that," said the leader severely. "I know – and so did everyone else – that you were referring to Sarah. Her mother explained the reason why Sarah couldn't come to the work party, and I'm satisfied with her explanation."

"I still think it's jolly unfair," Jenny muttered to Laura later.

"Well, perhaps Sarah won't want to come on Saturday," replied Laura. "She never seems to want to do anything that's arranged for the Guides."

But Sarah was there on Saturday afternoon. The weather was perfect – cloudless blue skies and glorious sunshine which made the water of the pool sparkle enticingly.

Lady Cavershaw came out and met the party of Guides. She suggested that they lose no time in taking a plunge into the pool.

"My granddaughter, Trudi, will be joining you," she said with a smile, as a curly-haired little girl ran up, clad in a bright pink swimsuit. "She has only just become a Brownie, so she thinks it's great fun being a Guide for the afternoon!"

"I'm going to be a Guide as soon as I can," put in Trudi, who wasn't at all shy in the presence of the bigger girls. "I'm taking my Brownie Swimmer's Badge. Watch me jump in, Grandma!"

Lady Cavershaw laid a restraining hand on the small girl's shoulder. "Now Trudi, I promised Mummy that you would only go in the pool when there was someone else in there to look after you."

"We'd better hurry up then, girls," laughed Captain, leading the way towards a cedar summerhouse which doubled as a changing room.

Soon the Guides were splashing merrily in the long, blue pool. All except Sarah, who sat on a bench watching the fun.

Bubbly little Trudi urged her to join them. "I thought all big girls could swim!" she called.

"I – er – well – I'm not very keen on swimming," faltered Sarah.

Trudi delighted in leaping into the pool, arms outstretched, trying to copy the Guides who could dive.

"That kid's going to be good one day," declared Laura, who was herself a very neat diver. "There's no fear in her at all."

"Not like some," added Jenny pointedly, noddling in the direction of Sarah.

When it was time to change for tea, Trudi pleaded with her grandmother to let her stay in the water.

"No, Trudi," Lady Cavershaw said firmly, "you must come out now and help hand round the cakes to your new friends. Remember, that was supposed to be your good turn for the day."

Trudi pulled a cheeky face and climbed out of the water. She followed Lady Cavershaw slowly towards the house, while all the Guides ran to the changing hut. None of them bothered to speak to Sarah, who remained by herself on the bench.

A few moments later, a little pink figure darted back to the poolside area and flung herself once more into the water. Sarah got up, intending to speak to Trudi when she surfaced and remind her of what her grandmother had said. But no curly head appeared. With a horrified shock, Sarah realised that the small girl was lying on the bottom of the pool.

Without a thought Sarah kicked off her shoes and jumped into the water. Her clothes dragged

around her heavily. She gulped a deep breath and dived down to where Trudi lay, and hauled her to the surface.

"What's going on over by the pool?" Jenny asked Laura, as they emerged from the hut to shake their hair dry in the sun.

"It's Sarah!" cried Laura in alarm. "Perhaps she's fallen in!"

They raced to the pool and were soon helping Sarah to get Trudi out of the water. By this time, Captain had noticed what was happening and was there to administer first aid to the little girl. The other Guides watched with concern until they noticed Trudi's eyelids flicker and her breathing begin to function properly.

"Thank goodness you were there, Sarah," said Captain. "Run and get those wet things off. Jenny – you and Laura go with her. She may feel a bit shaky after what has happened."

"You can put on my tracksuit," offered Laura. "I brought it in my bag."

They found a towel that was less damp than the others, and watched as Sarah slowly took off her wet clothes. She peeled off her tights, and Jenny bit back a gasp of amazement. Sarah's legs were covered in ugly dark scars.

She tried to turn away, but Sarah had seen the expression of horror on her face.

"I was burned in a fire," she explained simply. "We lived in a flat in London before we came here, and one night it caught fire. My mother was in bed ill – she has a weak heart, you see. I managed to get her out and then went back for my little brother. But was too late – he died."

"That's why I have to wear those hideous tights, and why I mustn't hurt my legs," Sarah went on in a rush. "I didn't want anyone to know and make a fuss. The newspapers made a big thing about the fire and me being a heroine and so on – but I just want to forget it. I'm not a heroine, I'm a failure. I couldn't save Danny!" She burst into tears.

"But you saved little Trudi," Laura added. "You aren't a failure – I think you're marvellous!"

"Does Captain know – about the fire, I mean?" asked Jenny hesitantly.

"Yes – my mother phoned her the other day. We had to go to the hospital to see the plastic surgeon. That's why I missed the work party. I keep having to have check-ups on how the scars are healing."

There was an awkward pause. Then Sarah spoke again.

"I'm sorry I haven't been much of a Guide so far," she said, turning to Jenny. "You've no idea how I hate not joining in things. I tried to make myself come to the barbecue, but the thought of the fire –"

"Forget it, Sarah," Jenny told her with a smile. "It's me who should be apologising for misjudging you. Come on – we're missing that delicious tea – and while we're eating it, we can make some plans. Daffodil Patrol is going to be the tops from now on!"

Written and photographed
by Michael Edwards

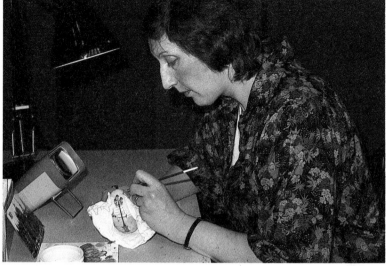

Valerie Rogerson at work.

Most people, given a goose egg, would either boil it, fry it, make an omelette out of it, or perhaps try to hatch it. But Mrs Valerie Rogerson wouldn't do any of those things. For Valerie, who lives with her husband, Ian, and their four children in the Lancashire hills above Whitworth near Rochdale, is one of this country's leading goose egg artists.

It all started ten years ago at Whitworth Comprehensive School, where she was an art teacher. "I wanted something different; something that was not too difficult but would keep the class interested," said Valerie, who chatted to me while she worked.

She remembered there was a goose egg in a cupboard at home and decided to have a go at painting it, and take it into school when finished. But the completed masterpiece never saw the classroom, as Valerie explained. "I enjoyed working on it so much that I didn't take it to school, and within a month I had completed 20. They were displayed in a large cabinet in the lounge."

Whereas most of her fellow egg decorators follow the traditional Czech style of pattern, Valerie's work includes oriental designs, fairytales and landscapes. But Shakespeare is her favourite

Goose eggs in napkin rings.

A medieval scene.

A Breughel scene.

source of inspiration. Her most delightful eggs have depicted scenes from *A Midsummer Night's Dream* and *Romeo and Juliet*. The Dutch painter, Breughel, has influenced some scenes.

"My versions of Dickens were a disaster. I once did a group of Kate Greenaway-type children dancing round a maypole and they were awful. Now, from experience, I know which scenes work and which don't. To be effective, the designs must be simple. Large groups of people would be very difficult to control, and complicated architecture gives me a headache because of the perspective."

Valerie likes to incorporate a figure, however small, somewhere in each picture. Landscapes with trees give height and depth; changing skies, seascapes and snow scenes for mood. Horses also figure in many of her pieces.

This kind of work has gradations of colour and shade which can only be achieved with water colour. When dry, she can shade one colour into another, which would be impossible with any other medium.

Apart from the best quality cartridge paper, there's no

surface quite like that of a goose egg. Its matt, somewhat porous texture, gives the paint something to 'bite' on.

Obtaining goose eggs was a problem at the start. Little did she know that geese only lay between February and July; and that most eggs are sold for hatching.

"To begin with, I got most of my eggs from local farmers, but that wasn't a good idea because I had to take what was offered. Invariably they were addled, which isn't a pretty sight when it comes to emptying out the contents."

She uses a drill to make the holes for blowing. It is crucial that the drill does not go beyond the interior skin of the egg, or it may crack.

Valerie is most particular about the shape of the eggs she uses. "They must be perfect. Not too rounded or too elongated – a classic egg-shape, in fact. The shape and even the size of the eggs varies tremendously, depending on the time of year and the age of the goose. Double yolkers are far too big."

Although she has an ostrich egg, she has never considered painting it. "Not only is it too large, it hasn't the same surface as a goose's egg and the shape is wrong. Hens' eggs are too small, while duck and turkey eggs are unsuitable because of their smooth shells."

At first, she had problems when the paint wouldn't take to the shell

A selection of completed eggs.

which, being porous, it should have done quite easily. It was caused, she discovered, by the oils from her skin clogging the surface. Now she hold the eggs in tissue paper and prefers to work with the eggs in her hand, rather than use a stand.

For displaying goose eggs there is nothing quite like a napkin ring. Plain, simple but very effective as you can see. However, some are hung from stands.

Some scenes work, some don't. If, after many hours of struggling she can't achieve the required effect, she vents her frustration the only way she knows how – she jumps on it!

A Trip of a Lifetime

By Jenny Mounsey

Imagine being able to visit the very first Guide World Centre, Our Chalet, at Adelboden in Switzerland! Not very many people get the chance, but amongst those who did were Guides of the 2nd Guiseley Company, led by Jenny Mounsey, who took these photographs.

Destination in sight at last – time for a rest.

Nearly there! See how narrow the mountain roads are: ones like this are used by cars.

If you have good eyesight, you may be able to see that *two* flags are being flown by Our Chalet – the World Flag, and a Swiss pennant.

View across the Engstligen valley, to the village of Adelboden, location of Our Chalet.

Last-minute tidying up before meeting our hostess.

Enough steps for everyone to have their picture taken in comfort.

A mountain stream feeds a constant supply of water to this drinking trough.

Listening to our hostess telling us the Chalet Story.

One of the dormitories with the trough-like beds, or 'mattrassenlagers' popular in this area of the Alps. (The hats belong to a group of Guides from the United States.)

Preparing for the Promise Ceremony at which Wendy is to become a Guide.

"Welcome to the worldwide sisterhood of Guiding."

Wendy with her Patrol Leader.

The Choleren Gorge, just down the valley from Adelboden, is very impressive, and well worth a visit.

A closer view of the front of Our Chalet, to show the beautifully carved wooden panelling.

Our Chalet in its summer setting of green slopes and fir trees.

The FIRE BRIGADE

By Debbie Scholes

Photographs by Joan Randall

9...9...9... "Which service do you require – Fire, Police or Ambulance?"

"Fire!!!"

Most people probably take our Fire Brigade for granted, but anyone watching the newest recruits at the London Fire Brigade's Training Centre in South East London would realise the seriousness of it all. Training at the centre takes fourteen weeks; in this time the recruits learn how to use most of the appliances needed by a fire fighter.

Marie Conroy and Julie McDarby of the 2nd Catford Ranger Unit attended the passing out parade of around twenty new recruits on a chilly, wet day in November. The alarm bells in the neighbouring fire station rang six times, calling the recruits on to the parade ground. This parade takes place in front of proud parents and friends, when the recruits are handed their certificates and trophies at the end of their training.

After the presentations come the displays of courage and expertise when the newest members of the London Fire Brigade are put through their paces.

Training at the centre begins with the recruits learning how to handle each individual piece of equipment separately, from the hoses to the ladders. Then, as we were to see, their knowledge is pieced together, until finally they can deal with any emergency they may be called to.

To promote a team spirit, the trainee fire fighters carry each other up and down ladders and through windows, to practise rescuing people from burning buildings. You may have heard of a 'fireman's lift' – this is the name for the safe way to carry someone in these situations. While the training is in progress, the pretend 'victim' will be tied to a length of rope in case of accidents; but in a real life incident, the fire fighter has no such safety device. He or she must take extra care that they do not drop their load; it's no good rescuing a person from a burning building and then dropping them halfway down the ladder!

Hoses were used to control an imaginary 'fire' during this and later demonstrations, and these 75 feet long rubber tubes were unrolled and furled again in seconds. The recruits demonstrated that no fire fighter goes into a blazing building or other potentially dangerous situation alone, and must always report where they are going.

In another demonstration, where smoke bombs billowed clouds of very realistic-looking smoke from the third floor, ladders were used to show how the hoses are pulled up the outside of the building with ropes, enabling the fire fighters to provide a jet of water to put out fires on each floor. A later demonstration showed two volunteers with breathing apparatus and protective suits entering the smoking building to bring out a cylinder. These can explode like bombs if overheated, and may also contain poisonous chemicals. In such a situation the fire fighters construct a pool of water to put the cylinder in, using sheets of plastic, ropes and planks of wood. When they have removed the cylinder from the building, it is placed in this pool until the fire has been extinguished and the danger has passed.

The last exercise came as an excellent reminder that the fire fighters are not only trained to deal with fires, but also with a multitude of other emergency situations, including road, rail and aircraft crashes, floods, and people trapped in lifts, tunnels – even heads stuck between railings!

Marie and Julie were allowed to view the appliances at close hand, after the recruits had demonstrated the results of their successful training to the audience. The two Rangers also viewed the vintage appliances in the museum, some of which dated back as far as 1848 or even earlier! The first known 'fire engine' is believed to have been just a long pole with a hook at one end: the hook was to pull off thatch from a roof; thatch, of course, burned very easily.

Facts about the Fire Brigade . . .

- The London Fire Brigade is one of the largest fire fighting and rescue operations in the world.

- The Fire Brigade say that you should always dial 999 and call them on suspicion of a fire, even if you don't think that it is very serious. They would far rather have a wasted journey to a fire which has already been successfully extinguished than allow someone to die or know that property has been damaged. The Brigade attends every call it receives, however small the incident is.

- The specialist equipment used by the Brigade includes electric and pneumatic cutting gear, emergency generators and lighting and hydraulic lifting equipment.

The initial training at the Training Centre may take only fourteen weeks but, after leaving Southwark Training Centre, recruits must serve for four years at a fire station before they are considered full fire fighters.

Anyone who is interested in becoming a trainee fire fighter must be at least 18 years of age. There is a minimum height requirement of 5' 6" and a minimum chest measurement of 36" which must expand by at least 2" on inhalation. Applicants must also have good unaided eyesight.

The London Fire Brigade is especially interested in hearing from girls who wish to become fire fighters – this could be a career to think about.

it's Valentine's day!

By Jil Shipley

Go for a very pretty look today! Tie up your hair with pink ribbons and rags and scraps of lace! Wear your heart on your sleeve — or on your collar — most stores sell a variety of appliqué hearts — buy a few and play about with them!

Love hearts

Whisk an egg white, add 45g. icing sugar and mix well. Divide into two, and add a few drops of pink food colouring to one half. Flavour with rose water, orange or lemon juice, raspberry or almond essence. Roll onto a board dusted with icing sugar and cut with a heart-shaped cutter. Leave to harden.

Make your own Valentine card with pink card and a real lace frill. Write the message in glue and sprinkle it with silver glitter.

I love you!

Sew heart-shaped buttons up the side-seam of your trousers. Sew heart-patterned ribbon round the top of your socks!

Biscuit hearts

Cream together 100g. each of butter and sugar, add 1 beaten egg and 225g. plain flour. Mix to a firm dough. Leave in the 'fridge for 30 mins (if you have time). Roll the dough thinly, cut out shapes with a heart-shaped cutter and bake at 190°C (375°F. gas mark 5) for 10 mins. When cool cover with white icing (icing sugar and water) and sprinkle with silver balls.

J.S.

Midsummer Day! Celebrate with flowers!

Put flowers and ribbons in your hair!

Sew fake(or real!) flowers around your hat!

Sew single blue forget-me-nots onto a pale pink t-shirt.

Have a picnic in the garden!

Sew a little bunch of daisies onto a velvet ribbon and wear it round your neck.

Decorate slides and hair grips with tiny flowers and pretty ribbon bows. Wrap ribbon round slides and stitch into place, then sew on flowers.

Serve food on sticks – chunks of raw vegetables – carrots, peppers, celery, tiny mushrooms, tomatoes, with a big bowl of mayonnaise to dip, followed by chunks of fresh fruit, dipped in lemon juice to prevent browning, peaches, apricots, pears, apple, plums, pineapple, with a bowl of sour or fresh cream and one of sugar.

Have bunches of wild flowers and grasses in a jam-jar on a cloth on the lawn.

Make a Midsummer Day posy for Mum! Cut a hole in the middle of a paper doiley, thread a bunch of flowers through the hole and secure with thread or sellotape from behind. Wrap the stalks with silver foil.

Sew individual tiny flowers onto a thin ribbon to tie around your ankle. Sew a bunch of flowers onto the front of canvas pumps.

d.s.

41

Have a Hallowe'en Party!

Make the theme 'black and orange' — have orange balloons and cover the table with black crêpe paper. Fasten back the doors and hang long strips of orange and black crêpe paper from the door frames. Cut out witch shapes from black card and hang them from the ceiling with invisible sewing thread and blu-tack, or blu-tack them to the windows. Buy lots of incense (joss-sticks) for atmosphere! Wear fluorescent orange net in your hair — dye a huge white t-shirt orange and paint witches' hats on it with fabric paint. Paint a moon or a star on your cheek with metallic face paint. Paint stars and moons and witches onto plain white paper cups. Have a table centre-piece of a cabbage, cut so that it stands straight, covered with silver foil and stuck with cocktail-stick snacks. Try pineapple chunks wrapped with thin strips of carrot, celery filled with cream cheese and chopped walnuts, melon balls, alternating chunks of cheese, apple and cucumber, dill pickles and rolls of salami or garlic sausage — experiment!

Sew sequins onto black tights — wear with lurex leg — warmers and black pumps.

Make a pumpkin or turnip lantern. Cut a 'hat' off the top and hollow out the pumpkin or turnip with a knife (be careful!) and spoon. Put a nightlight or torch inside and put it in a dark corner — scary!

J.S.

Christmas day with the family

Start the day off well by giving Mum tea and toast in bed! Decorate the tray prettily.

Pretty-up your dress by adding a lace collar. It's just 70cm. of lace — cotton lace is nicest — gathered at the top to fit the neckline of the dress, and then lightly tacked on.

Give everyone a surprise extra gift! Just something tiny — perhaps a few sweets — nicely wrapped in a cracker, made by covering a cardboard roll with crêpe or tissue paper, fastening the ends with elastic bands and sticking on a hand-made label. Put them on the lunch table.

Wear a long velvet ribbon for a belt, tied in a big bow in front.

Give your shoes a festive air, with bows made with lurex ribbon!

Contribute to the food with these delicious marzipan dates. Blend thoroughly 100g. icing sugar, 100g. caster sugar, 225g. ground almonds, 5ml. lemon juice, 1 egg, few drops almond essence. Add a little green colouring. Knead until smooth and use to stuff stoned dates. Top with whole almonds.

J.S.

P.S. Wash some dishes!

Goathland Station

The Railway Camp

By Margaret Baird

Photographs by Nigel Robertson

The Guides cheered and waved as the coach pulled away from the Church Hall to take them to camp. Sally pressed her face up to the window so she could wave to her mum and Mark, her younger brother. Mark was jumping up and down with excitement, pulling on his mother's hand.

The coach turned the corner and Sally settled back into her seat. It was her first camp, and she had been looking forward to it for a long time. Her friend, Judy, was sitting next to her. They were in the same Patrol, the Chaffinches.

Mrs Barnes, their Guider, handed out a piece of yellow paper to each Guide. Sally read hers. It said:

Railway Camp Challenge
We are going to camp near a steam railway. How many of the following activities can you complete by the end of the week?

1 Draw a sketch map of the railway track from Grosmont to Goathland.
2 Name five wild flowers growing near the railway.
3 Find out when the railway was built.
4 Plan a walk along the Railway Trail. Draw a sketch map of your route, including anything of interest that you notice.

"Steam trains!" exclaimed Sally. "I've never seen one before. When I go on the train to Leeds, it's one of those diesels."

Judy didn't say anything, just stared out of the window.

At last they reached the camp site where they were going to live for the next seven days. As they were unloading all the tents and kit bags, they heard a puffing noise.

"It's a train!" shouted Sally, and the Guides ran down to the bottom of the field and looked over the fence.

The train came chuffing round the corner. It had a green engine pulling red carriages, and as it passed the Guides it whistled.

"Let's wave to the passengers," cried Sally, and everyone waved madly.

"Isn't it great!" said Sally turning to speak to Judy, and she suddenly realised that she hadn't come with them. She looked up the field towards the camp, and saw Judy up by the pile of equipment with Mrs Barnes. The Guides trooped back up the field and a moment later Mrs Barnes blew her whistle and gathered everyone together.

"There's an instruction card for each Patrol," she said, giving them out to the Patrol Leaders. "You should be able to pitch your Patrol tents by lunchtime, and finish everything else this afternoon."

Sally joined her Patrol by their tent bag. While they were at camp their Patrol was to be called the Red Engines. The others were the Blue, Green and Yellow Engines. As they took out their tent, they discussed the Camp Challenge.

"'I can't wait to have a ride on a real steam train," said Jo as she measured out the guy-line pegs with a mallet. Jo was the Patrol Leader, and an experienced camper.

"Shall we plan a Patrol hike for tomorrow?" asked Sally.

Jo was showing the others how to fit the tent poles together. "Yes, that's a good idea," she said. "I'll ask Barnesy if we can make some sandwiches to take with us. We could go one way on the train and walk back."

Suddenly Judy threw down the bag of tent pegs and ran up the field. The rest of the Patrol

The camp from the train

stared in an amazed silence. Then Jo spoke. "What's wrong with Judy?" she asked.

Sally watched Judy disappear into the store tent which the Guiders had put up. "I don't know," she replied. "I'd better go and talk to her."

She found Judy inside the store tent. As she walked in Judy jumped guiltily, and then knelt down and pretended to be looking through a box of plates and cups.

"Is anything wrong, Judy?" asked Sally.

Judy plucked at the grass, hesitated, and then stood up.

"No . . . I'm alright," she said. "Come on, we'd better help the others with the tent."

Later on, after the Guides had eaten their packed lunches and done all the jobs on their cards, they had half an hour's free time.

Judy was whittling a stick with her camp-knife. "I might not come on the Patrol hike," she said quietly. "I'll ask QM if she wants any help in the store tent."

Sally looked at her. There was something wrong. Usually Judy was so eager to join in with everything.

"Judy, what's wrong? You can tell me, I'm your best friend."

Judy's reply was drowned by the loud whistling of an approaching train. Some of the Guides ran down to the fence, and Sally and Judy stood up and watched as the train chuffed by. A moment later Mrs Barnes blew her whistle so Judy had no opportunity to tell Sally what was worrying her. The Guides gathered around Mrs Barnes to hear what she had to say.

"Cooks, will you help QM, please? Wood and Water, we need more wood, as much as you can find. Health, will you make tripods for the wash tents, please. Mess Patrol, put out the sitters and anything else that's needed for the meal, please. Right, off you all go."

"Would two of you go for the milk, please?" said Mrs Dunlop, who was QM for the week. Sally and Judy volunteered, and set off for the farm with the milk churn.

It was warm and sunny, and the farmyard was still and quiet. Several kittens basked on the hot paving stones. The farmer's wife saw the two Guides, and opened the kitchen door.

"Come for your milk?" she asked. "I've put it in the dairy for you."

She showed them the way into the dairy. The cows had been milked and the bulk milk tank was full. A churn of milk had been saved for the Guides. The farmer's wife gave the two girls a glass of milk to refresh them.

"Gosh, I've never had such fresh milk," said Judy. "It tastes different when it isn't in a bottle."

The farmer's wife laughed. "You town girls need it," she said. "It'll put some colour in your cheeks."

After tea, when everything had been washed up and cleared away, Mrs Barnes organised a game of rounders, and then it was time to put down the beds in the tents.

As Sally unrolled her sleeping bag and pulled on her pyjamas and a thick jersey, she thought for the first time of home, and how Mark would be having his bath, and listening to a story

The Guides wave as the train goes past

Along the journey

while he sipped hot milk from his Peter Rabbit mug. But Sally didn't feel homesick; she knew it would all be waiting for her when she went home next week.

Judy was next to her in the tent, and was already asleep by the time Sally had wriggled down into her sleeping bag. In the next tent some girls were giggling and chattering, but they stopped when Mrs Barnes blew the 'lights out' whistle. After all the excitement and fresh air, Sally felt quite drowsy, and in no time was fast asleep but, just as it was beginning to get light, she woke suddenly. Sitting up, she heard muffled sobs beside her.

"Judy!" she whispered. "Are you all right?"

The sobbing stopped. Judy sat up, her face tearstained. "No, I'm so worried about tomorrow, Sally. I don't know what to do!"

Sally felt in her rucksack and pulled out a tube of mints. "Here, have one of these. Now, tell me what's wrong."

Judy pleated the blankets between her fingers. "It's the train," she said at last. "I've never been on one before, and I'm frightened of it."

Sally stared at Judy in amazement. She couldn't believe that anyone could be eleven years old and never have been on a train.

"But there's nothing to be frightened of," she said. "I love going on trains!"

Judy shook her head, and started to cry again. Sally wondered whether to wake up Jo, but then a torch flashed outside the tent. It was Mrs Barnes.

"Everything all right?" she asked, looking in through the tent flap. In the torchlight she saw that Judy was upset.

"Come on, love," she said. "Put your wellies on and come into our tent for a while. QM has a

flask of hot milk. You'll soon go back to sleep after that."

Sally curled up again in her sleeping bag, glad that Judy was being looked after. She dozed off, trying to think of a way to help her friend. Then she heard Judy come back into the tent, carefully stepping over the sleeping girls.

After a while Judy whispered to her, "It's all right now. Mrs Barnes says I can come and wave you off at the station, and then help her back here. Goodnight!"

The next morning, after the Red Engine Patrol had finished all their duties, and been inspected, they set off on their Patrol hike. Mrs Barnes walked down to the station at Grosmont with them, so that Judy could go back with her. The Guides had a leaflet with them about the railway, and a map of the area.

The path to the station was covered with cinders, and the Guides spotted several wild flowers straight away. They found Herb Robert, a small purple flower, and Tormentil, a tiny yellow flower with four petals. Judy seemed much brighter, and joined in with all the chatter.

While they waited for the train the Guides filled in the time by browsing in the shop. Sally bought a badge with a red steam train on it to give to Mark. Then they heard a puffing noise and the train steamed slowly up to the platform. Judy stepped back against the wall, and Mrs Barnes moved next to her. "Don't worry," she said. "Nobody's going to make you go on the train."

The rest of the Red Engine Patrol climbed up the steep steps into one of the old brown and white carriages. The guard shut the door, and blew his whistle.

"See you later!" shouted Sally. "Have our tea ready!"

The train pulled slowly out of the station, the Guides waving to Judy and Mrs Barnes. Then they settled back in their seats to watch the countryside go by. As the train went by their camp site they all jumped up and waved to the other Guides.

The train arrives at Pickering Station

"We can find out when the railway was built at Goathland station," said Jo. She showed the rest of the Patrol the route she had planned. They were going to walk back from Goathland to Grosmont, stopping to eat their packed lunches on the way.

All too soon, the train pulled in at Goathland station. The Guides jumped down onto the platform and went into the waiting room. A poster on the wall stated that the railway was first opened in 1836.

Then they walked up the hill into Goathland village, where Jo bought a bag of apples for them. After taking their bearings, they set off for Beck Hole, which was halfway home.

Listening to the others laughing and chattering to each other, Sally missed Judy, and wished she had come too.

Then Jo caught up with her, and offered her an apple. "Let's have lunch at Beck Hole," she said. "It will make our rucksacks lighter."

They reached the village, and found a picnic spot down by the river. The ducks enjoyed scraps of bread from the cheese sandwiches.

Jo bit into a crisp green apple. "What a shame old Jude wouldn't come," she remarked. "She doesn't know what she's missing. Still, I'm frightened of heights myself, so I can imagine how she feels."

Sally felt glad Jo had said that. She didn't want the others to think her friend was a baby.

After clearing up the remains of their picnic, the Guides went to look at the little sweet shop and cafe by the bridge. Jo asked if they could use the toilet, and Sally shut herself in without the light behind a door which said 'GIRLS' on it. Stifling giggles, they went back into the sweet shop and bought a bag of jelly babies. Then they set off back towards Grosmont. Their route took them away from the railway, across some stepping stones, and past some little cottages. As they trekked along the road Sally began to feel rather tired, but perked up when Jo started to sing, and soon they were all marching along singing *Swinging Along the Open Road*.

"Round this corner, and then we'll see the camp site," said Jo, following the route on the map with her finger. Their way took them back round towards the railway line, and as they walked along the trackside path, they found the rest of their five wild flowers; Jack the Pulpit, Convolvulus and Foxgloves were growing all along the hedgerows. Then they heard a familiar puffing noise. Another train was coming!

The Guides leaned on the fence and waited for it.

"Don't forget to wave!" Sally shouted to the others. Then, as the train thundered past, she saw a small figure in blue, waving madly at the window.

Sally turned to the others.

"I'm sure that was Judy!" she cried. "Quick, let's run on to the station and meet her!"

Tiredness forgotten, they ran along the path, past their camp, and on towards Grosmont station. Soon, up ahead, they saw Judy, walking back to camp with Mrs Barnes. She was smiling, and when they met up, she showed them a red metal badge on her t-shirt. It was a little red engine.

"I'm a proper member of the Red Engine Patrol now," she said. "And I'll never be frightened of going on a train again. It was fantastic!"

Mrs Barnes laughed, and told them how, after they'd left, one of the engine drivers had offered to show her and Judy round the workshops, where the engines were repaired. Judy had seemed so interested that he'd offered her a free ride to Goathland and back.

"I couldn't refuse," she said. "I remembered the Guide Law, a Guide has courage and is cheerful in all difficulties, and the next thing I knew I was on the train!"

That night, as they were sitting round the camp fire, Mrs Barnes told them about plans for a holiday to the Guide Chalet in Switzerland.

"I hope you will all be able to come," she said. "It's a long journey to Our Chalet. We'll be going by train all the way from London, to Basle in Switzerland."

Judy nudged Sally. Her eyes were shining.

"I knew Mrs Barnes had a reason for helping me to go on the train," she whispered. "Next stop for me is our Chalet!"

The North York Moors Railway is one of the world's earliest railway lines. It was built by George Stephenson in the 1830s to link the seaport of Whitby with the rich farmland of the Vale of Pickering. In 1965 the route was closed by British Rail, but eight years later it was re-opened as a private railway.

The railway is operated by a non-profit making charitable trust, and you can ride on the railway, hauled by steam trains and diesel locomotives representing every type of loco design from 1890 to the present day. The line runs from Pickering to Grosmont and is open every day from April 1st to October 31st.

Musical Moments

By Hilda Young
Illustrated by Belinda Lyon

A glimpse into the lives of some well-known composers

The Silver Penny Part

Like many musicians before him, while he was trying to gain recognition for his work, Richard Wagner was often very poor, never more so than during the winter of 1842 as he waited to see if someone would perform his opera *Rienzi*. Wagner was forced to sell his furniture to pay the rent, while his food was provided by kind friends.

Even when the news came that the opera was to be performed in Dresden, Wagner had to borrow the money for the fare, and he wondered how on earth he was going to live during the rehearsals.

His problem was solved in a very strange way. At the theatre one of the singers was so impressed by a part of the score that he insisted that each member of the company paid Wagner one silver penny for the honour of singing that part. Each week the silver pennies were handed over to Wagner, who used them to pay for his board and lodgings.

Even when he later achieved great musical honours he always remembered with gratitude *Rienzi* and its 'silver penny' score!

Haydn's Farewell

Josef Haydn was a fine musician, but also a warm-hearted and caring man. For a large part of his musical career he was the musical director to Prince Nicholas Esterhazy, a great patron of the arts.

During the summer months, the prince insisted that all his musicians accompany him to his summer palace, in order to play to his guests.

Unfortunately, there wasn't much room for large families in the palace, and although Haydn had a comfortable home there, his fellow musicians had to leave their families behind, which distressed them very much. Too afraid to complain to the prince, Haydn decided to highlight their plight in a musical way.

He composed a symphony in which each instrument in turn stopped playing, until there was absolute silence. And not only did each musician stop playing as his part in the music ended, he put out the candle which had illuminated his score, and quietly left the stage. At last only Haydn remained.

The prince was an intelligent and sensible man and he realised that this was a musical 'strike', and instead of being angry he was amused at Haydn's cleverness.

The next day the entire party returned home, and the musicians were reunited with their families . . . thanks to Josef's clever idea. His *Farewell Symphony* is still played today.

The Ghost in the Attic

When George Handel was a small boy, his father refused to let him play any kind of music because he had plans to make him a lawyer. But, realising how unhappy this made the boy, a friend managed to sneak a clavichord up into the attic when George's father was out of the house.

This instrument could be played very softly, and George would go up silently into the attic and play when everyone else was fast asleep.

But one night his father awoke to the sound of ghostly music. Fearfully, with candlestick in hand, the barber-surgeon walked slowly up into the attic . . . to find his young son playing the clavichord.

At first his father was angry, but later, when a German duke overheard the boy playing and offered to pay for George's tuition from the Halle Cathedral organist, George's father was forced to recognise that his son had great musical talent . . . especially as he was not yet eight years old!

The Miller's Boy

Franz Schubert loved music from an early age, because he was taught to appreciate it by his schoolmaster father. However, when young Franz pleaded to

become a musician, his father was not pleased: he wanted Franz to be a teacher like himself, and so he said that he hadn't enough money for lessons.

After much thought, Franz had an idea. He asked to be allowed to enter the audition for a place at the *Stadtkonvit*, where boys received a first class education if they were accepted for the choir. Franz had a good voice and he hoped to win.

There were many boys trying for a place, and when they saw him dressed in a grey smock, some of the boys began to mock him, calling out, "Here comes a miller's boy in his flour smock. We have come here to sing, not to mill flour." But the examiners took pity on the small shy boy and asked him to sing.

Taking his courage in both hands, Franz sang the set piece and, as his pure voice rang out, everyone gazed in wonder. Here was a lovely voice indeed!

Franz was given one of the two available places . . . his life of music had begun!

The Christmas Mouse

Finally, there is a lovely story told of how the beautiful carol *Silent*

Night was composed.

Although not as famous as some composers, Franz Gruber will always be remembered as the man who set to music the immortal words written by the parish priest, Josef Mohr, in the little Austrian village of Oberndorf.

Josef Mohr was making a last minute inspection of his church on Christmas Eve in the year 1818 when he discovered that a little mouse had eaten the bellows cloth and the organ could not be played.

It was unthinkable that there would be no Christmas music, so the priest hurriedly composed his own little carol, and his friend the organist set it to music.

The choir was hurriedly called in to learn the carol and at Midnight Mass, to the sound of a guitar, one of the world's most famous carols was heard over the still night air for the first time.

It is still sung in many countries of the world, well over a century later, and even if people do not know of Franz Gruber, they *all* know his lovely music!

ALL DRESSED UP!

The Scout and Guide Committee have organised a Fancy Dress Disco. GSL Tony and his fiancée, Jean, Guide Captain, decided to give everyone a laugh by dressing as Noddy and Big Ears. They persuaded five other couples to join them for the evening. See if you can work out who the couples were, and what they were dressed as.

GEOFF	BATMAN	ROSEMARY	NURSE
ANDY	DOCTOR WHO	MARSHA	WONDERWOMAN
BRIAN	HENRY VIII	GEMMA	VICTORIAN MAID
OLIVER	SUPERMAN	JOANNE	QUEEN OF HEARTS
DEREK	CHIMNEY-SWEEP	HELEN	CINDERELLA

BRIAN and ANDY were cartoon characters, and went with JOANNE and the Nurse respectively.

GEOFF went as Henry VIII, HELEN as the Queen of Hearts. However, the King & Queen did not go together.

Superman went with Wonderwoman; MARSHA accompanied Batman.

OLIVER, who was not Doctor Who, went with the Victorian Maid, who was not GEMMA.

Check your answers on page 61.

Danish Juniors from Ribe go to Camp

By Muriel Dunn

While on holiday in Denmark, before Christmas, I was invited by one of my Guiding friends to take part in a meeting of the Junior Guides (aged 10 to 12 years). How delighted I was afterwards to receive a letter saying "Please come and join us at our summer camp".

School summer holidays begin quite early in Denmark, and so I set off by boat and train for Ribe on Saturday 23rd June. We all met at the railway station in Ribe on Sunday morning. Each girl had her own rucksack full of personal kit to carry, but the bulkier equipment, packed into large boxes, had been sent off to the campsite by train, earlier in the week. After 'goodbyes' to parents and friends, we caught the train to Skorping, in the north of Jutland. Our group was made up of seven girls, their leader, Lena (camp name Rufus) and assistant leader, Britta (Bo). Later in the week I, too, received a special camp name (Junior).

It didn't take long to set up camp, our leaders having chosen an excellent site. My knowledge of Danish was very limited, and the girls did not understand much English, but I managed to show by actions and sign language what was to be done. Rufus and Bo spoke good English, and helped out when any difficulties arose!

Breakfast was eaten together – bread and cereal, plus tea or milk to drink, but first of all came the early morning exercises! Yes, we *all* did them – a cross between yoga and 'O'Grady Says'.

Lunch each day consisted of Danish open sandwiches (rye bread topped with fish, eggs, tomatoes and such). Fruit and a glass of milk followed, and then rest hour. The evening meal, cooked in Patrols, was always a hot dish plus dessert.

On the first day, we concentrated on setting up Patrol washing lines, and a large pole to hold our red and white Danish flag. We practised the correct use of an axe and a saw, and then set up our kitchen area. Then it was time for a walk in the forest, to explore, and relax a little.

On Tuesday, the Juniors were shown around by the forest

ranger, who talked about the trees and wildlife of the area, and showed the girls how to press wild flowers, and use them to make greetings cards and book marks. Later that day they also had the chance to make bread dough, this time in Patrols. Flour, water and yeast were mixed together, and then left in a covered pan in a warm place. Unfortunately, one lot of mixture got too wet, and during the course of the evening it expanded, finally oozing out over the top of the pan, and even covering the box it was standing on! It almost seemed alive!

Before breakfast, it is customary to have flag break and prayers, and a 'Thought for the Day', but on Wednesday morning we were woken by singing: it was Rufus's birthday, and everyone gathered round to sing special songs, holding wild flowers,

Danish flags, and presents for her. Another special event was a trip to the Alborg zoo: this required some map reading and compass work by the girls. The highlight of our visit was the birth of a baby kid to one of the goats in the children's corner.

On Friday, the girls went on a long hike. After breakfast, helped by the Guiders, they packed everything they might need for an overnight expedition: cagoules, thick jumpers, spare socks, night clothes, toilet articles, a compass, torch and maps, plus some food, a cassette recorder, and an emergency telephone number.

The route they were to follow was marked on the map, and they were given details of questions to answer about the village, and people to interview and record on tape on the way. Rufus, Bo and myself ferried the bedding rolls by bicycle to the site where the bivouacs would be made.

Eventually, after a long journey, the girls met up with us at the hike

site; the bivouacs were built, and sausages roasted over the camp fire before going to bed. We three Guiders sat by the campfire and sang quiet songs as the girls quickly fell asleep.

Next morning it was hard waking them up for the hike back to camp, despite the promise of buying hot bread and Danish pastries en route. Sadly, I had to leave that morning, and everyone came to say 'Farvel' as my taxi arrived to take me to the station.

Thank you, Ribe Juniors, for inviting me to your camp, and for the super letters I have received asking me to visit you again. Thank you also, Lena and Britta, for sharing your Guiding with me. It was fun, and I would love to come to Denmark again some time.

MAKE A FROG POP-UP

By Karen and Chris Sheridan

YOU WILL NEED:

Plain paper
Light card (similar to the card used to make greeting cards)
Scissors
Glue
Felt tip pens (or crayons)

1. Cut out the whole page opposite. If you don't want to cut a page out of your Annual you can copy the design and colour it in yourself. (This frog is green but frogs can be many different colours.)

2. Cut a piece of card to the same size and fold in half.

4. As indicated, fold back the paper and crease along the diagonal lines. Then turn over and fold the flaps back the other way.

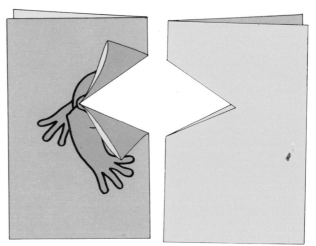

5. Now fold the frog flat, then fold in half again, so the frog design appears on the inside of the fold, and push the flaps in (see diagram).

6. Glue the back of the frog (but not the flaps!) and stick inside the folded card. As a fun addition you can write greetings and messages inside the mouth of the card – or draw an insect to be swallowed by the frog!

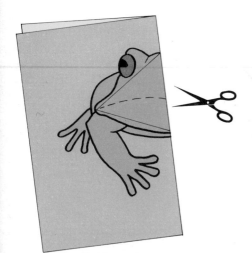

3. Fold the frog down the middle and with your scissors, cut along the line of the mouth.

The card is now completed and you will find that as you open and close the card the mouth of the frog will pop-up and open and close.

gland around it to keep the hair healthy, supple and able to repel water. Animals that live a lot in water, such as otters, have very oily fur. The shaft of the hair outside the skin does not grow but the root expands and adds to the length of the hair. Fortunately there are no nerves in a hair so it does not hurt when it is cut with scissors but it does if pulled away from the root.

Hair which becomes short of oil gets very dry and may break or die. Every hair only lives and grows for a while, then it falls out to be replaced by others. In the same way as birds feathers fall out when old and dead (moulting) so if you have a pet cat or dog you will know the cat's fur or the dog's hairs will moult, too, and be left all over the carpet and armchairs! When they are alarmed or cold, some animals can raise their fur to keep warmer or look frightening to an enemy. A cat will do this when faced with an annoying dog. Birds also ruffle their feathers to keep warm or look fierce. We have some hair on our body, such as the top and sides of our head, this helping to protect it from sun and other weather, but we cannot raise it to stand on end usually to frighten people, nor can we grow it thicker to keep warm. Of course, there have been people who have claimed their hair stood up on end when they saw a ghost!

Hair is used by many animals as camouflage, to disguise themselves, the patterns being formed by different coloured hairs. The hair of the sloth which lives in South America is so thick and tangled that often tiny mosses and ferns grow on it which help hide the sloth among the tree branches. Then there are certain animals – the Arctic fox, stoat and Scottish hare are some – which are white in winter to blend with snow and then in spring this white fur moults and they become mostly brown furred. Animals which live in hot countries may not have much hair as they do not need it. The elephant and rhinoceros are almost hairless, though the 'horn'

on a rhinoceros' head is really a tuft of thick matted hair, used for digging out roots and charging an enemy. Of course, some fur or hair, such as the wool of sheep and hair of camels, is used by man, made into clothes to keep us warm.

It is difficult to believe that the quills of a porcupine or spines of a hedgehog are in fact a sort of hair that has become very stiff to protect the body. The porcupine's quills will stand erect immediately the animal is frightened by an enemy and it will also shake the quills to scare off the enemy. There is long, soft hair mixed among the quills, too. On the hedgehog the spines also normally lie flat or nearly flat but

can be immediately raised when needed for protection. They cover all the body except the short head and stumpy tail, the head and underneath the hedgehog's body being clothed with coarse dirty brown or dirty white fur. The hedgehog gets further protection by rolling itself into a ball.

Another curious form of animal body protection is that of the armadillo of South America. It is a descendant of the huge prehistoric animals that lived thousands of years ago. Its body is covered with hard bony plates and horny shields. If danger threatens, the armadillo rolls itself up, tail shield and head shield fitting together neatly so it is protected on all sides, and there is no way an enemy can attack unless it waits until the armadillo 'ball' unwinds, thinking danger is past. The pillbug or woodlouse found in gardens uses a similar tactic and rolls into a ball.

Other creatures use scales to protect their body. Snakes have overlapping scales on their backs, like tiles on a house roof, but those on the underside have a keel and are like the rungs of a ladder. They are connected to the ribs of the snake and as the snake moves its ribs so it slightly lifts the scales and they are able to grip, which is the reason why snakes can move so quickly and silently and even climb trees, moving around the upright trunks as they grip the rough bark with their scales. In warm countries, like Africa and India, snakes can live a normal life all the time, but because scales do not keep a snake warm when the weather becomes cold in countries such as ours snakes hibernate

A Trip to the

DAILY Mirror

For the competition in the 1984 *Girl Guide Annual* we invited you to send in a report suitable for a magazine or newspaper on a subject connected with Guiding.

We had a great number of entries, and finally chose as the winner Jennifer McAllister, of the 2nd Croesyceiliog Guide Company. Jennifer and her sister Rachael, who is also a Guide, came up to London and spent an evening at the offices of the *Daily Mirror*. They were shown the editorial offices, where the journalists work on the articles to go in the next day's paper, and the teleprinters, each typing out news sent in from all over the world; they saw a machine that can receive photos over the telephone wire, and produce a copy good enough to be used in the paper; they saw the typesetting room, where the words are set up before being somewhere snug, in a disused rabbit burrow or among piles of leaves in a hedgebottom.

Other creatures with scales are fish, or most of them, though a few, such as the conger eel, do not have scales. The scales of fish are usually overlapping horny plates made of a material rather like our fingernails, to cover and protect the skin and soft body of the fish. The scales are pliable which means as the fish moves its body, swimming in the water, the scales bend slightly with it and the scales are kept healthy because the skin makes a layer of slime over them. This is the reason why some fish slip through the fingers so easily when picked up!

As a fish grows each year an extra amount is added to the edge of each scale and if you could see a scale under a magnifying glass you would notice these are like the rings of a cut log or tree trunk. The number of fish scale rings tell you how old the fish is.

Scales do not keep fish warm, but as they are cold-blooded creatures anyway this does not matter as their body is about the same temperature as the water around them. If it is a very cold winter some fish will go into deeper water or swim farther away from Britain southwards to where it is warmer, then come back again in spring.

Perhaps the oddest use of fish scales was several years ago, where the scales were removed from large fish, washed, dried and glued together to make into buttons for ladies' clothes!

---

sent down to the foundry where the printing plates are made; and they saw the huge machines down in the basement printing out hundreds of copies of the paper.

Jennifer and Rachael were probably the first people in Britain to see that edition of the *Daily Mirror*, still warm from the press!

Before starting back for Olave House in Kensington, where they were to spend the night, they watched as vans loaded with bundles of the paper left the depot; from there, copies would be distributed to newsagents all over the country.

The *Girl Guide Annual* would like to thank Mr Chapman and the staff of the *Daily Mirror* for their help in planning this feature.

Jennifer's winning article, which describes what Guiding was like in her grandmother's Company, some 60 years ago, appears below.

Thumbs Down for the 1920s Guide Uniform!

The first thing my grandmother recollected of her Guiding days of the mid-1920s was her dislike of the uniform. As there was no summer uniform, the girls were expected to wear thick, navy blue serge tunics all the year round, as well as black woollen socks. The Guide ties were, however, similar to the neckerchiefs of the modern Guide uniform, but were folded and tied at the back of the neck.

My grandmother attended the weekly two-hour-long meetings of the 16th North London Company at Stamford Hill from 1925 onwards. The emphasis on religion was then far greater than it is today. Meetings always began with prayers, and on practically every occasion the Company would be directly and very closely linked to a church, where Church Parade would take place once a month.

The evening would usually include performing drills, marching, practising lots of knots, and a considerable amount of time spent together as a Patrol. The atmosphere was, however, very much more formal than it is today, with even perhaps a hint of army discipline. The Guides were strictly trained to address their Guiders by the army derived names "Captain" and "Lieutenant", and never by their christian or surname, which is the practice found most commonly in today's Guide Companies. The "army" atmosphere was further emphasised by the air force style jackets, skirts and hats worn by the Guiders.

My grandmother recalls no "King's Guide" badges being awarded, either because they didn't exist, or because the girls didn't have enough time to earn badges.

There were never any outdoor camps, a commonplace activity today, as they were not approved of. The substitute was sleeping on "palliases" — mattresses filled with straw which crackled every time one turned over! — on a hall floor.

The Guiding of yesteryear was on roughly the same principles as today for the Guides, who paid 2d a week to belong to the Movement.

Kissing

By Simon Shaw
Illustrated by Caroline Bland

Kissing always has, and always will be, popular the whole world over. Small children kiss their favourite pictures in story books, and kissing games such as Postman's Knock are among the most popular entertainments at parties everywhere.

Kissing is even popular in the world of nature. Birds, goldfish, horses, rats, hamsters, porcupines and rabbits have lip-to-lip contact when courting for the mating season so that they get to know each other better.

Ways of kissing in greeting vary from country to country. In Britain, we kiss once only, but in France it's the custom to kiss each cheek, while the Russians hold each other in huge bear hugs and kiss three times. In India, there's a tribe which actually kisses three times on one cheek and three times on the other – and then follows this by passionately kissing both hands.

Some countries, however, insist that kissing should be done privately, never in public – because it's considered most immodest. So you'll never see Red Indians, Eskimos, Chinese and Malayans kissing. In Japan, kissing is even censored in the cinema where every kiss is cut by the censor just before actual lip contact.

Though some doctors believe that kissing is good for the health since it increases the heart rate considerably, others consider it to be a dangerous practice. In America, it's been found that even the lightest brush of the lips raises the heart rate from 72 to 95 beats a minute, so that one American doctor calculates that each kiss knocks 17 seconds off our lives, whilst a really passionate kiss can cut our lifespan by five minutes!

Some really strange things have happened to people when they kissed. A girl student gave her boyfriend a kiss on the ear, and its effect actually ruptured his eardrum.

In one home, a husband and wife had to give up kissing for a while as they installed a new nylon carpet. It seems that they received a painful shock from static electricity when their moist lips came into contact.

Many dentists see a connection between kissing and the state of your teeth as many bacteria pass between partners' lips as they kiss.

This connection between teeth and kissing can also lead to action in court. In New York, one woman had her wisdom teeth removed, but afterwards found that she no longer enjoyed the kisses of her husband; the court later granted her £10,000 in damages – and her husband £7,000 – for the loss of pleasure they used to get from a kiss.

One London taxi driver whose jaw was broken in a car smash was given £12,000 damages against the man who crashed into him because he was unable to kiss anymore.

Records have been set for kissing. The world record-holder is a man from Alabama in America who kissed 3,567 girls in eight hours, one every 8.07 seconds. One pop singer kissed his partner 25,009 times in just two hours to win a bet for fast kissing.

In the cinema, the longest screen kiss so far was between Jane Wyman and Regis Toomey in a 1940 film called *You're in the Army Now* – they kissed for 185 seconds. It's worth studying Cary Grant and Ingrid Bergman too, in some of their films, if you want to see some lingering kisses.

One kiss caused a scandal the world over, when the greatest sculptor of the last century, Auguste Rodin, created his *Le Baiser* (The Kiss) statue. It was first shown to the public in 1886, and people thought it was so outrageous that in London it had to be fenced off in case the public threw stones at it. In Tokyo, it was hidden behind a bamboo screen, and in Paris Rodin was charged in court for producing such an immodest piece of art.

But in America, the statue was so well received that one wealthy man offered Rodin part of his fortune to make a copy of the statue for him to keep in his home.

If you want some scientific facts on kissing, one French woman studied it as she prepared for her degree in Paris – and she came to the conclusion that kissing, Western-style, involves the exchange of 9 mg of water, 0.7 g of albumin, 0.18 g of organic matter, 0.711 mg of fats, and 0.7 mg of mineral salts between partners – all of which makes up one of the most pleasurable experiences for everyone in the world.

The Lady of the Light

Written and photographed
by Michael Edwards

Peggy Braithwaite's house is situated at the end of a long, bumpy and twisting track which finally loses itself among the sand dunes on the Isle of Walney, off the Cumbria coast.

I had listened carefully to the coastal weather forecast during breakfast, to be told that, "There will be winds at sea; south-east, force seven increasing eight, veering south-west later. Visibility moderate to poor. Sea state, rough."

Gale-force winds, salt spray and blowing sand wasn't exactly what I or the two Guides (Loraine McVinnie from 25th Barrow St Mary's Walney Island, and Louisa Corbett from 33rd Barrow St Columba's) had expected, after being told that Mrs Braithwaite's home was in the sand hills by the sea. But it was, after all, the end of October.

We had ventured into this weather-beaten environment to visit the lonely lighthouse which dominates the scene. There Mrs Braithwaite greeted us, for Peggy is the only lady lighthouse keeper in Britain.

"Lighthouse-keeping is a Braithwaite tradition," she explained, as we sat in the cosy lounge of her tidy white cottage as the wind howled outside and the sea crashed over the beach. "I followed in my father's footsteps. He was an assistant keeper and

The Guides first sight the lighthouse across a sheltered bay where a small fishing boat bobs at its moorings.

The Guides pass through the low gate in the wall which prevents blown sand accumulating in the cobbled yard. The 'cobbles' are in fact beach pebbles of varying sizes.

later principal keeper at Walney. During the War, when the lighthouse wasn't operational, the assistant's house was requisitioned as an officers' mess. When the war ended, many women were doing men's jobs and my sister, Ella, came on the staff as assistant keeper. When my father died, my brother-in-law was taken on, and by 1948 I was already on the staff as an auxiliary keeper under my sister. But when she died in 1967, I was promoted to principal keeper."

Lighthouses were originally privately owned. To build one, you had to apply for a royal charter. The Port of Lancaster Commissioners did so in 1788: a charter was granted and Walney lighthouse was built in 1790.

Soft, white sandstone ferried from the Commissioners' own quarry at Overton, near Lancaster, was used and brought to the site in flat-bottomed barges towed by schooners. Some of the sandstone blocks were six feet square and it is rumoured that the foundations go down forty feet.

The Guides approach the lighthouse and cottage along a rough track through the sand dunes. Note the wall on the left of the picture, which prevents the dune spilling over onto the track and blocking it.

The pebbles presented varying patterns and textures which Loraine found made an interesting photograph.

When the lighthouse was built, the port of Barrow didn't exist. It was constructed to assist the Jamaican sugar schooners which made a landfall here before steering to Glasson, where the Port of Lancaster Commissioners had big docking facilities. Today the light is used by most traffic plying the Irish Sea.

Walney was the first lighthouse in England to be fitted with revolving reflectors – and the last to retain them. Now, most lights have prism lenses with the light behind.

vacuum cleaning and ironing half an hour before lighting-up time while the engines were warming up. In summer, that meant I was doing my chores at 9.30pm. But it also taught me to be economical with electricity because I never left a light on that wasn't needed, in case it put an overload on the generator."

The lighthouse was connected up to the national grid in 1969, but it still has generators on stand-by. The only difference is that now an electric drive motor replaces the wind-up, but the bulbs are still the same: 250 watt projector types which, in front of their reflectors, give 450,000 candle power. That may sound powerful, but it is only a baby compared with Eddystone or Fastnet. Walney light issues one flash every fifteen seconds.

The sophisticated radio beacon situated in one of the stone out-buildings is supplied by Trinity House, which also issues a radio and a stop-watch to enable Peggy to get the Greenwich time signal at whatever time is convenient every morning and evening.

stop. The motor runs on a normal domestic electricity supply, but the bulbs are reduced to 110 volts DC to give a steadier light. Two transformers are used on alternate nights, making complete system failure virtually impossible.

The phone rang. It was the coastguard to inform Peggy that the lifeboat is being launched at 1pm for a trial run.

Louisa asked Peggy if she has a busy season.

Peggy Braithwaite greets the Guides on their arrival.

Question time in the lounge as the Guides bombard Peggy with questions.

Last summer, in recognition of her services, Peggy received the British Empire Medal in the Queen's Birthday Honours List. It is an award of which she is quietly very proud.

Until 1952 it was lit by acetylene gas, and driven by clockwork, which consisted of a drum with a wire on it going down over pulleys to 100cwt of lead, which had to be wound up periodically through the night. If the gas failed it took twenty minutes to put in emergency paraffin lamps.

"When we went onto home-made electricity we had only 600 watts per house for domestic use once the light was lit," explained Peggy, "so I did my

The radio beacon transmits the code F N in morse code four times, followed by 25 seconds long dash, whereby ships beam onto it for navigation. Then it will transmit F N twice followed by two minutes five seconds silence during which period Point Lynas and Douglas Head transmit, because Walney is in a triangle with those lighthouses.

A small motor called a creed governor operates an alarm should a bulb fail or the motor

Peggy explains the function of the Radio Beacon. The two clocks at the top of the beacon act simply as visual aids should the beacon fail during the night when you can't receive the Greenwich pips.

Loraine inspects Peggy's interesting collection of picture postcards of lighthouses from different parts of the world.

"Yes," replied Peggy, "April to October. We call it the silly season, when people go out in ill-equipped boats with insufficient petrol for their outboard motors and no alternative means of propulsion. It's like going on a long journey without a spare wheel."

Loraine then asked if the weather causes any damage to the lighthouse. "Not to the lighthouse itself, though blown sand can make the glass very dirty and in cold weather a frosty glaze may form on the inside which I have to remove with de-icer."

Peggy is responsible for general maintenance. "We, my husband Ken and I, paint all the boundary walls with Snowcem, and the house and outbuildings, plus 36 windows and 47 doors with white gloss. My sister Ella used to paint the tower, but now we employ an outside contractor."

"But isn't being a lighthouse keeper a lonely life?" asked Louisa.

"Not at all," replied Peggy. "One can be very lonely in a city if you don't know anyone. It is much better if you can stand your own company in a job like this; at least if you ask a question of yourself, you know that you will get a sensible answer," she laughed.

"I like the environment, I enjoy the responsibility which the job entails. I like to think that I am doing something useful. I'm really not as cut-off from civilisation as many people think. Although

Walney is an island, it is connected to the mainland by a bridge, so I can travel by car into town every weekend to do my shopping.

"There will come a time when I won't be capable of doing the job any more. When that times arrives I will have to think of going somewhere else ... at the moment I would settle for Woburn Abbey, if I have a choice," she joked.

"When you live in a lighthouse you can't help having an interest in them, but Ella and I were also very keen on competition ballroom dancing. We did swimming and diving too, and some years ago I took up judo. Once I was very interested in car mechanics and rebuilt my own car. Oh, and I like studying the weather.

"I knit and sew, I like writing letters; beach-combing is enjoyable and I am interested in all types of wildlife. I have recently conducted a plant survey of the area and got up to 184 different species," she told us enthusiastically.

"I like bird-watching, too, but I wouldn't sit in a hide all day. That's probably because I can watch them from various windows. In winter, many kinds of birds come into the garden for shelter during their migrations, including many

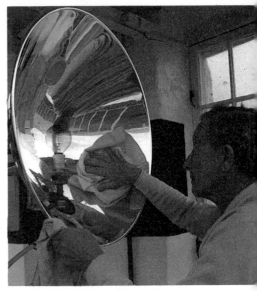

Peggy polishes one of the silver-plated copper reflectors which are cleaned every day, as are the windows. In the lamphouse on a sunny day it is so hot that Peggy is forced to carry the reflectors to a lower landing to clean them because the wax dries before it will polish. We were rather surprised by the small size of the bulbs.

Hold onto your hats: Peggy takes the Guides onto the beach where they beachcomb for firewood as the sea thrashes and foams.

The Guides take a closer look at the marram grass which helps bind the sand, preventing the dunes from being blown away. The fine, spreading roots enable the plant to withstand galeforce winds by gripping the sand and forming an extensive root mat. Peel Island, with its castle, is in the background.

Goldcrests, Britain's smallest bird."

The lighthouse is situated in the 230-acre South Walney Nature Reserve, and during the spring Peggy's constant companions are gulls, 40,000 pairs of which make their nests in the dunes to form what is believed to be the largest colony of its type in Europe. "The birds are one reason why I am never lonely," added Peggy. "It can be cold and very bleak in winter but when you live on the edge of the Irish Sea that is only to be expected."

A couple of years ago an unusual bird crossed the path as Peggy was going to the village. She mentioned it to the reserve warden. Later, she learned that she had seen a Richardson's Pipit, a very rare visitor to Britain which had only been seen twice before.

The following day hordes of bird-watchers from all over Britain descended, clutching telescopes and binoculars. "I don't think any of them saw it," smiled Peggy, "but when I went to take my dogs for a walk in the dunes, I saw it again."

Her favourite bird is the Oystercatcher, unmistakably feathered in black and white with a long, orange beak which it uses to prise mussels, not oysters, from the rocks. They also eat cockles

and sand worms.

Most Oystercatchers lay their stone-like eggs among the shingle, well above the tide line, but one bird chose to make her nest too near the water's edge and was in danger of being swept away by the tide. But by moving the bird's eggs a little higher up the beach each day, Peggy overcame that problem and the Oystercatcher hatched her eggs in safety.

Due to the light, the area is good for moths, and Peggy is helping to complete a moth map of Britain to enable naturalists to pin-point the best areas for these insects.

Lighthouse keepers are a self-sufficient race – Peggy grows her own vegetables with varying degrees of success – they have to be. But there may come a time when keepers are no longer needed, as more and more lighthouses are becoming automatic.

"All that needs to be done is to change a bulb and report it," said Peggy. "That may happen here some day, unless lighthouses become redundant altogether with so much sophisticated navigational equipment available."

But until that happens, Peggy climbs the 91 steps to tend the precious light perched 75 feet above the sea twice every day for as long as she is able.

The Girl Guide Annual would like to thank Peggy Braithwaite and her husband, Ken, without whose assistance this feature would not have been possible.

The nature reserve is equipped with a number of observation hides . . . a perfect place to get out of the gales on the day of our visit. In summer, nesting sea-birds may be watched from it and even whales and porpoises in the deeper water off-shore.

The sight of summer: the sand dunes surrounding the lighthouse are dotted with thousands of nesting gulls. The red and white striped posts mark the nature trail.

The Oystercatcher, Peggy's favourite bird, incubates its eggs in safety on the beach. Visitors to the reserve must take care not to tread on the camouflaged eggs.